PORTRAIT OF A VILLAGE

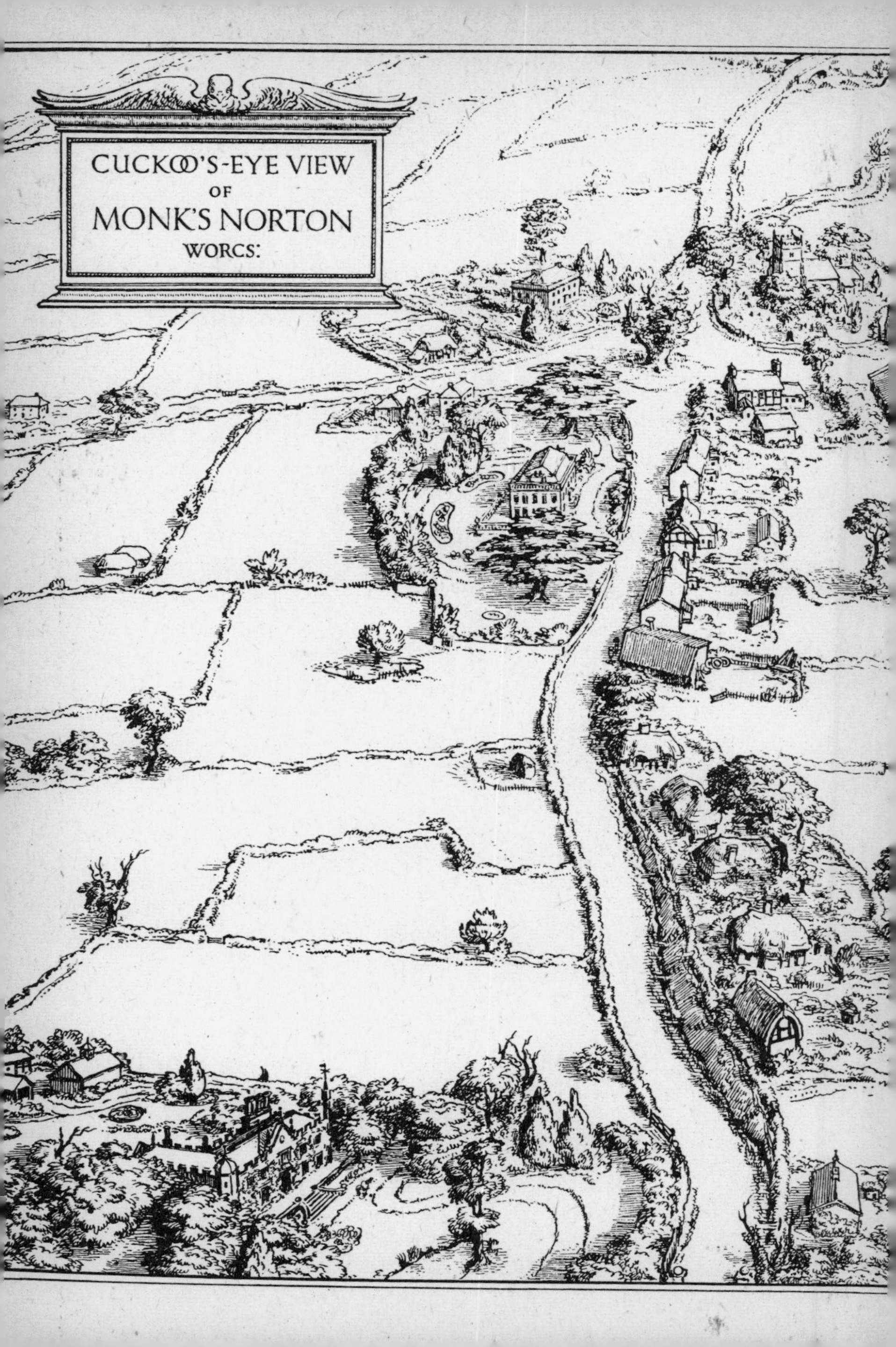
CUCKOO'S-EYE VIEW
OF
MONK'S NORTON
WORCS:

Joan Hassall

THE
SHELDON
ARMS
AS

PORTRAIT OF A VILLAGE

FRANCIS BRETT YOUNG

ALAN SUTTON
1983

Alan Sutton Publishing Limited
17a Brunswick Road
Gloucester

First published in 1937 by William Heinemann
This edition first published 1983

ISBN 0-86299-104-8

Cover picture: detail from Evening – On the Severn *by Benjamin Leader. Worcester City Museum Service*

Printed and bound in Great Britain
by Redwood Burn Limited, Trowbridge

FOR
ELEANOR AND ROBERT HOLLAND-MARTIN

AUTHOR'S NOTE

Some years ago, when I published a book called *This Little World*, I was assured, by a multitude of correspondents, that they knew not only the village of which I had written but the people whose portraits I had essayed. Needless to say, when I wrote it, I had no actual village in mind; and never in my life have I been so foolhardy as to write of living people. It is the same with Monk's Norton. I take this opportunity of declaring that no village like it has ever existed outside my imagination; that the people whom I have devised for its inhabitation are, equally, wholly imaginary; that the names attached to them have been chosen from among those of places, or dredged from deep memories of my childhood, and have no connection whatever with any living soul by whom, for all I know, they may be borne.

F. B. Y.

CONTENTS

ENGRAVINGS ON WOOD

ENGRAVINGS ON WOOD

PRELUDE

PRELUDE

IN mid-Africa about the beginning of March, the greater rains having passed, the green veld suddenly grew pale. The grass was about to die; so that now, when the South wind blew over its surface lately dappled with tassels of purple like a summer sea, the waves wore a wintry look and their sound was wintry too, being no longer the voice of living green in motion but a whisper of stems brittle and dry. For days on end there was never a cloud above them. The sun sucked up every drop of sap that remained, and the stalks cried in vain to the roots for more, since the earth itself was parched and cracked like the lips of a man lost and dying of thirst.

Then the hairy caterpillars, which all through the rainy season had fattened themselves on the sapid grass-lymph, grew sleepy. Their skins became horny through lack of moisture; some instinct told them that they must prepare for a new stage of life. So, loosening their feet from the dry grasses, they fell to the ground in the night and crawled into the cracks which the heat had made, resigning themselves to that dreamy existence which is the life of the chrysalis amid the chambers of scorpions and ants and tarantulas, and caves where puff-adders and cobras lay coiled in their winter sleep.

In one frosty night all the hairy caterpillars were gone; and next morning, when dawn reddened the veld, the cuckoos which fed on them went hungry. Bewildered and angry the cuckoos scanned their pastures with bright, greedy eyes, and scrabbled with their dusky, yellow-edged beaks about the roots of grass, searching for any caterpillar that might have been slow to seek shelter. The cuckoos flew hither and thither without a cry; the only sound they made came from the thrashing of their wings. But the great pied storks, who were equally hungry, took their troubles more calmly; sedately, with measured steps, they paced to and fro or stood fixed in contemplation, as though they expected their favourite food to reappear. At evening, when the restless cuckoos still harried the sky, the storks gave three hops and spread their floppy wings. Rising slowly, like herons, they beat their way to a flat-topped acacia, and sat there, like a council in conclave, debating the question. And next morning, when the cuckoos resumed their fruitless foraging, not a stork remained.

After a while, the cuckoos, which (save in the shelving of domestic duties) are silly birds, discovered that what they had regarded as a temporary hitch in the caterpillar-supply was a permanent breakdown. By this time they had become too hungry for anger: even the wallows and waterholes where they had been accustomed to drink were sinking, and beset with rude strangers from farther South who were more thirsty than they. So, at last, when the veld caught fire from the sun and acres of tindery grass roared away down the wind in a sheet of flame, the male cuckoos took to the air and fled Northwards into the night, blindly following the track which the storks and the clouds of swallows had traversed before them.

Those cuckoos flew high, invisible in the cool upper air. The glower of the bush-fires faded beneath and behind them; and now, having once been launched on their flight, they forgot the distress of hunger and thirst. They flew on and on: over steaming lakes where myriads of flamingos preened their rosy breasts and shrill ospreys fought for a silver fish in mid-air; over spent volcanoes, whose throats were clogged with a moss of forest; over one great mountain-cone, fluted with glaciers, where an eddy of icy air dragged their strong wings downward; over a swollen river, wider than any they had known and unlike all others (for cuckoos' memories are short) because it flowed Northward. East and West of it lay deserts coloured like a lion's hide; but along either bank stretched a ribbon of irrigated land—green, piercingly green, in which surely caterpillars must be found: so that some cuckoos, moved by false reasoning rather than faith, dropped down and came to rest on the shoulders of two stony, man-made monsters, who had sat there for centuries solemnly gazing Eastward—until savage bees, that stored honey in a crevice of the stones, came angrily swarming about them and drove them away. And after that waspish guerrilla a demon wind rose, half-solid with blown sand, blotting out the green tilth below and the sun above. It caught the cuckoos helpless and swept them along in its black, gritty heart. Like driven leaves they were whirled away; and when the dust thinned, their sand-sore eyes beheld not land but leaden water: a running sea, streaked with white foam, and a huge ship riding it.

Many birds were circling that ship: hoopoes, kestrels, swallows. And now, faint with useless effort, five cuckoos, who found themselves left alone, dropped down and clung to the masts with their woodpecker claws: but the steel spars were too smooth to give hold, and though four scrambled on to the rat-lines, one fell to the deck, where a Chinese quartermaster caught him fluttering in the scuppers and carried him into the galley to boil for his supper.

All day the ship drove ahead with a running sea on her starboard bow; and by sunset, when the wind had blown itself out and declined to a Southerly waft, the four remaining cuckoos, having rested their wings and sipped water from a rain-puddle, grew restive to feel that the vessel was carrying them away from where they knew they should go. Already the swallows and hoopoes and kestrels had vanished, and night was falling; so once more the cuckoos launched themselves on the sky.

Through all that night and the day that followed it, they were carried dreamily Northward on the drift of tepid air—over flat seas and lands grey with olive-groves, with which, as they knew, they had no concern (save one who, rashly descending, swerved into a net spread for quails), till the upper sky packed with shredded cloud, and a new wind arose whose buffetings spurred them on to wield their wings more bravely: for the smell of the lands beneath them was now familiar, having been infused into their ancestral memory for generations. It was an odour of briny spray and of meadow-grass growing lusher and greener than the stiff grasses of Africa: but, though hope sustained them, the goal of their flight was still distant. For two days and two nights they flew on, until, of a sudden, the white scimitar of a lighthouse-beam slashed the night and dazzled them, beyond which (as vague memory told them) ran the river-valley where all three had been hatched and fledged before they flew South: that valley, abounding in hairy caterpillars, towards which their instinct still led them.

As yet this valley could only be smelt, for the mist lay low; but when the sun, breaking through, burned the mist away, the green bounty of those almost-forgotten lands lay smiling beneath: a chequer of green fields, dark spinneys and blossomed orchards, with Severn, a thread of steel, flowing seawards between them. East and West rose the hills confining that ancient firth: the scarp of Cotswold cut like a cliff and the sharp ridge of the Malverns, with Bredon Hill, an island set in the midst. Here Avon flowed slowly past farmsteads of stone and half-timber girdled with elms; here the tall tower of Worcester, piercing the city's smoke, caught the fire of dawn in its lace of stone; here the wolds of the Lenches rolled Northward, scattered with foxy covers; and out of them, gradually twisting and ebbing away downhill towards Avon, the Brandon Brook cast a silvern snare about the village of Monk's Norton: a group of black-and-white cottages clustering on either side of a cross-roads and dominated by the squat sandstone tower of the parish church.

As those cuckoos flew over Monk's Norton, a cracked bell in the church-tower struck a leisurely six, followed, twelve seconds later, by the clock above the stables at The Grange, retired, fifty yards away, on the village's outskirts. As the sound died away on the still April air, the three birds, which had flown together in silence for over five thousand miles, with one accord parted company. One dropped to the field called Long Dragon Piece, hard by Goodrest Farm. The second flew straight to the belt of elms which embraces "The Cubbs" at the back of the

Sheldon Arms. The third slid swiftly towards a tall lime tree whose shadow fell on the eastern wall of The Grange. This last, less tired than his fellows, broke silence as he flew. *Cuckoo,* he shouted, *cuckoo, cuckoo, cuckoo!* And the others lazily answered him.

THE CROSS

I

The Cross

MONK'S NORTON, as seen from a great height by the cuckoo's eye, is a reasonably compact little village, its irregular shape of thatch and lichened tiles resembling nothing so much as a splash of faded ink on green blotting-paper or a shadow of motionless cumulus dappling a green field. Dr. Hemming, who has flown over it, proposes a comparison less poetical but possibly more apt. To him it suggests the shape of certain living cells under the microscope: a dark nucleus, representing the packed concentration of buildings about the cross-roads, where only the church, the Manor House, the Rectory and the Inn stand apart, and a surrounding area of buildings, less densely congregated and therefore paler.

No matter which of these figures be the more picturesque, the doctor's is nearer truth in one way; for Monk's Norton is certainly alive. It has been living, according to monkish record, ever since, in the year of Our Lord seven hundred and sixteen, Ethelbald of Mercia granted the manor of '*Nortona juxta Wiccium*' to Abbot Ecgwin of Evesham, and it became not merely Norton but Norton of the Monks. For more than two hundred years the Church enjoyed its manor, its berewicks, its fishpond, its mill, its warren and thirty hides of land; but by the time of Domesday, the Norman had got his teeth into it: the manor, and all the rest, having been snapped up by that wolfish sheriff Urse d'Abitot, so that nothing was left to the poor monks of Evesham but their share in the village's name, which remains to this day.

Since this remote excitement, history, which is mainly concerned with unpleasant and violent events, has consigned Monk's Norton to centuries of happy obscurity. The gangster feuds of the warring roses seem to have left it untouched; the Black Death, in its visitation, deprived its church of no more than two harmless incumbents; and even if Charles II actually slept at 'The Goodrest' after Worcester Fight (which is highly improbable considering the lie of the land and the number of other houses which claim to have housed him)—even if the cannon-ball which gives its name to Warstone Farm was truly discarded by Cromwell's siege-train, it is doubtful whether the folk of Monk's Norton took any great part in the struggles of King and Parliament.

It has always, in fact, been rather 'out of the world,' and seems likely to remain so. Though main railway-lines run North and South on either side of it (on still nights the thunder of heavy freight-trains can be heard in the distance) the nearest station is five miles away, and few trains stop at it. No high-road of greater importance than one of the ancient salt-ways, which lost its identity before the last pack-horse vanished, has ever run through it. The main thoroughfare, which enters it by a narrow bridge spanning the brook, marked as 'unsafe for heavy vehicles,' comes to an end at the white gate of The Grange; while the one minor road which crosses this is soon cut on the East by a cressy watersplash, impassable in seasons of flood, and on the West by an even more formidable obstacle: the North Bromwich and Worcester canal.

This isolation on what is, in effect, a peninsula thinly girdled by stagnant and flowing waters, has limited the growth of Monk's Norton. In more turbulent times, no doubt, its watery encirclement gave the village a certain security; to-day, when violence no longer threatens its peace, the same element discourages expansion. And though, indeed, Monk's Norton has never shown any disposition to expand, it seems not, by the same token, to have noticeably contracted. During the last century, ever since the navigation-men cut the canal, its population has rarely been more or less than two hundred souls: a self-sufficient, self-centred and (almost) a self-supporting community. Neither the pride nor the pains of ambition have modified the tenour of their existence. The village offers to the outer world no spectacular beauty of landscape or singular work of Art. No outstanding man has lent lustre or infamy to its name. Its very normality and humility have protected it; with the result that it remains to this day more typical—in itself and in its inhabitants—of a kind of life that is fast disappearing than any of its neighbours: a village of un-industrialized England perpetually preserved (as a fly in amber) in its limpid, crystalline matrix of Severnside air.

. . . . .

The shape of Monk's Norton, conditioned by its bony skeleton of two metalled roads, only the greater of which is tar-sprayed, is roughly that of a cross, with four major buildings—the church, the rectory, the inn and the Manor House—standing back from the junction of its arms. Here a widening of all four corners has left room for a considerable island of green turf, in the midst of which stands a hollow oak so bleached and stricken in years that its annual burgeoning appears a miracle. Whether Charles II dossed down at 'The Goodrest' or no, he could certainly have spent an uncomfortable hour or two in this monster's branches. Fred Perry, the publican, whose signboard and advertisements of Astill's Entire they conceal, considers the decrepit tree a disgrace to the village as well as a handicap to trade. He would like to see it replaced by some military trophy—a rusty British tank or German field-piece—to remind him of the days when he, and the rest of the Second Worcesters, wound up the Watch on the Rhine, or, at least, surrounded by a circular bench on which customers might sit of a summer evening and drink his beer. A few years ago he 'brought up the matter,' he will tell you, at a meeting of the Parish Council in which the forces of reaction and sentiment, represented by Mr. Follows the Rector, and the last surviving Miss Abberley, inflicted on him and his friends a crushing defeat—the more unreasonable in that neither of the tree's defenders (thanks to the rampant laurels that screen the mossed drive of the Rectory and the rampart of clipped yew concealing the lower half of the Manor's Carolean façade) is compelled to look at the blessed thing as he is. One day last Winter, Mr. Follows, who has a way of poking his nose into everything, discovered a salmon-tin containing dregs of saltpetre which had been upset in the hollow of the trunk to hasten its disintegration. Mr. Follows and Miss Abberley were both convinced that Fred Perry, or some ruffian hired by him, had maliciously put it there; but Sid Homes, the policeman, who respects both the rector's cloth and Miss Abberley's gentility and considers Fred Perry, with whom he plays cricket in Summer, a personal friend, confessed himself unable to smell out the culprit. And the oak recovered, anyway.

Apart from this standing grievance, over which, from time to time, he makes himself ridiculous, and the streak of native obstinacy of which it is a symptom, Fred Perry is a weak, pleasant, intelligent, generous man, and an excellent citizen. When he 'flies off the handle,'—as he does, sometimes, over politics, his wife puts it down to the War into which he was plunged twenty years ago at the age of eighteen. As a rule, Mrs. Perry, a comfortable practical woman, who is more expert in the vagaries of his nature than he, knows how to manage these outbursts. She herself was a nurse in a V.A.D. Hospital when first they met, and the marriage, a month after the armistice, has been, in the main, a happy one. Now that their children are growing up—the boy is well on the way to a Brewing degree at the North Bromwich University, and the girl is in London qualifying to nurse babies 'from the month'—she is able to devote her quiet reserves of energy to Fred and his business. Her husband is proud of her education and her refinement—she was a tradesman's daughter, and distinctly above him—no less than of her commercial capacity, to which he cannot pretend. He is also proud of her appearance. Though she is a year or two older than he and of a matronly amplitude, she is still a 'fine figure of a woman' and has not wholly lost the charms with which, as a slim girl in a nurse's uniform, she first attracted him.

He is proud of the Sheldon Arms too, as well he may be; for the Perrys, father and son, have held the licence for three generations. If he no longer, as did his forbears, buys malt and hops and brews his own beer, the house is still free and no man is his master: when the brewers' travellers arrive he is able to deal with these tyrants on equal terms and to speak his mind. In the conduct of the house he is no less independent. The door of the public bar opens and closes on time; no customer who has not proved himself able to carry his liquor is served, and none dare dispute the decision. As for the Sheldon Arms itself, though the house is old-fashioned—a rambling, low-ceiled building of warm brick and timber, with floors of foot-worn flags and surprising variations of level that trip an unsuspecting tread—the interior is a paragon of order and cleanliness, permeated by vague alcoholic odours of beer and spirits and cider which give its air a faint antiseptic tang. The public bar, in which the commonalty sit, is as austere, with its table and benches of scrubbed oak, as a monastic refectory. The bar-parlour, behind whose mahogany counter Mrs. Perry sits sewing or knitting, and which communicates with the other by means of a hatch, is the cosiest room in Monk's Norton. In Summer its open casements, commanding the 'cross,' admit wafts of cool air: in Winter a brisk fire burns perpetually on the hearth, its clear flames reflected in gleaming brass and dull pewter, in the coloured ranks of bottles of spirit and liqueurs that stand on the shelves, in the lustre jugs and in the polished glasses whose crystalline clearness is Mrs. Perry's particular pride. The small room is panelled and furnished with shining black oak, and the walls are undecorated save by four coloured prints of cock-fighting scenes ('worth a mint of money'), a carbon photographic enlargement of Fred Perry throwing out his chest in his sergeant's uniform, a chromo-lithographic seedsman's-almanac portraying a Derby winner, auctioneers' bills announcing current stock-sales, and a number of cards (which Mrs. Perry's delicacy regretfully tolerates) proclaiming the prowess and fees of shire-stallions at stud.

Here, every evening, the Perrys receive their intimates, and the affairs of the village are discussed in the spirit of an exclusive club. Here they sit and smoke and talk and drink temperately until the grandfather clock in the corner (by Jas. Milward, Bromsberrow), gives a click and a burr and solemnly strikes the hour. Mrs. Perry sighs and lays down her knitting; Fred knocks out his pipe on the grate. The cronies rise from the shiny benches and stretch their legs. "Well, well, time to be getting along. I reckon it's going to freeze: the wind's gone up North.

Good night, Fred." "Good night, Captain." "Good night, Mrs. Perry." "Good night. . . ."

Mrs. Perry methodically collects the glasses and swills out the dregs. The 'girl' will rinse and re-polish them in the morning. Fred, under her watchful eye, pours out a thin nightcap of whisky and shepherds reluctant customers out of the public bar. When he returns from locking it, Mrs. Perry has put out the lamps and lit two candles. Fred yawns as he takes them from her and lights her upstairs. He has no grievance in life—apart from the obstinate persistence of that wretched oak-tree.

It isn't, Fred Perry frequently maintains, as if there weren't plenty of evergreen trees in the centre of the village already. There are far too many for a man who has been gassed and needs air. Miss Abberley's huge Lebanon cedar, shadowing the Manor lawn, leans over the wall and steals the sunset light from the Inn's best bedrooms. On the corner diagonally opposite, the rectory garden boasts two shabby Wellingtonias, a horse-chestnut and a monkey-puzzle rising from unkempt shrubberies that harbour moisture all Winter; while the churchyard is girt with a bodyguard of gigantic elms, whose roots run down deep into the stiff Keuper marls and the subsoil of clay (which the huntsmen curse galloping over the ploughland in Winter) and whose tops house a garrulous colony of rooks.

The elm, indeed, is the typical tree of the Monk's Norton landscape. Apart from that noble central group which draws its sustenance from the bones of the village's dead, and another rookery, the remains of a depleted avenue leading to The Grange, superb and solitary examples are scattered over all the surrounding fields, and wiry pollarded elms have been left in the hedgerows as wind-breaks. As soon as one of these lonely monsters comes crashing down in an October gale, Mr. Beaseley, the carpenter, wheelwright and undertaker, has his eye on it and picks it up cheap, and stores the sound wood to season. His petrol saw-bench can deal with heavy timber, and there is nought like elmwood for coffins. Not that many coffins pass through the lychgate in a year. Five or six at the most. Monk's Norton folk normally live to a very great age and dodder on, writhen and rheumatic, until, like the old elms, they fall. Even in death the elms embrace them.

Apart from this one heavily-treed area about the cross-roads, the main street (it is un-named) of Monk's Norton lies open to sun and sky. In its upper part, beyond the Inn yard and gabled outbuildings, the houses preserve a certain air of stylish formality. All save one—Dr. Hemming's, which is black and white half-timber, with the legend *W.S.* (? Sheldon) *1619* carved in fair seventeenth-century script on a distorted beam over the doorway —are built of the same soft and glowing brick, and date, one would guess, from much the same period as the Manor. A little later, perhaps; for the upper windows, which have not, like the lower, been replaced by shop-fronts, show the proportions and amplitude of the age of Queen Anne. They are occupied, as one might expect from their central position and judge from their neatness, by a superior class of people.

First of all comes the draper's and haberdasher's shop, which the protruding "Public Telephone" sign (and little else) announces as also the Post Office. Mrs. Bentley, the sub-postmistress, who has been a widow for more than ten years, and still carries her mourning beneath her starched apron, is a bright little old lady with exquisite manners and a tiny voice, whose brisk movements and pipings resemble those of the canary whose cage swings over the counter. Her shop, in which the commerical side is divided from the official by a wooden partition with a gate in it, is low-windowed and so dark that one wonders how she can find her way among the cardboard boxes of stock or sort letters and deal with her postal returns; but Mrs. Bentley's eyes are so used to it that she can put her hand on a packet of pins or a sixpenny postal-order without a second's hesitation. Her sphere of activity is so small that she is mistress of every inch of it. A born gossip, without the faintest suspicion of malice, she is a greater repository of secrets than anyone else in the village, Dr. Hemming not excepted. The mail which she sorts is an encyclopædia of conduct and a directory in one. Without moving a yard from her counter she is able to discover which young men are interested in horses and which in football pools; who is in love with whom and with what degree of response; where her neighbours' grown-up children are working and to what extent they do their duty by their parents; who pays cash and who is in debt and being dunned; who is coming to lunch at The Grange or The Manor on Tuesday next, and where Mrs. Perry (the glass of fashion) got the new dress she wore in church last Sunday.

Though these intimate excitements of the present engage her secret mind, her talk, oddly enough, is mainly concerned with the past. She often speaks of her late husband, whom she naïvely calls 'father'; and 'what father always used to say' still carries with her the authority of Scripture. How she lives, with such beautiful self-respect and decency, remains a mystery; for the Postmaster-General rewards her work (if he also provides her entertainment) with a pittance. Perhaps her son, who is a shop-assistant in North Bromwich, or her daughter, who married a Scotch head-gardener, occasionally sends her postal-orders which she cashes for herself. Perhaps, in that tiny, cage-like existence, her physical needs are so small that she can live by pecking, like her pet canary. The bulk of her trade must surely have left her counter since George Mason's bicycle-shop down the road blossomed into a garage and he bought the top-heavy brown bus which, three times a week, carries women with baskets of butter and eggs and dressed poultry to Worcester market, and boys and girls to 'the pictures' and Woolworth's buzzing counters. Most of her stock is out-moded. The plain, stalwart, old-fashioned hairpin, guaranteed to keep a bun firmly fixed through a hard day's washing, is lost on this flimsy generation of bobs and shingles; while whalebones for corsets are no more in request than black mending-wool for stockings, garter-elastic and boot-laces.

Mrs. Bentley's main visible means of support (apart from the Post Office) has consisted, since 'father's' death, of the rent derived from her upper floor, which is let unfurnished to Miss Martin, the schoolmistress, who also acts as choir-mistress and organist and occasionally takes charge of the house when Mrs. Bentley goes out. Very occasionally indeed; for the conduct of the telephone-exchange in itself is not merely a full-time job, but one in which Mrs. Bentley takes a personal interest as a form of entertainment comparable to the wireless which she cannot afford. The only time at which she 'goes out,' in a little widow's bonnet spangled with jet, is after office hours: on Sundays, three times, to church, and on long light evenings in Summer to lay flowers on 'father's' grave. Considering her lack of light and of exercise, it seems extraordinary that Sarah Bentley remains as healthy as she looks and is. Yet she rarely ails; Dr. Hemming has never set foot in her little back bedroom since 'father's' death. No doubt her minute, incessant, bird-like activities suffice (like the canary's) to keep her spare little body in trim. And unlike most of his patients, the doctor remarks, she does not over-eat. For the best of reasons.

Miss Martin, the postmistress's lodger, occupies a compact flat of two little rooms with a third which is hardly more than a box (where she does her own cooking on a blue-flame oil-stove) on the floor above the post office. Her front room, thanks to the spacious Queen Anne window, which looks over Miss Abberley's tawny-walled garden to distant hills, and the cream distemper with which, to Mrs. Bentley's anxiety, she has covered and brightened the dingy wallpaper, is as light and airy as the post office below is dim. It resembles no other room in Monk's Norton. There is, as folks say, hardly a stick of furniture on the beige cord carpet: nothing but two Morris chairs of fumed oak, a draped divan, a range of sectional bookshelves and a writing-desk. "Not so much as *one* ornament!" the village gasps in astonishment. There are, it is true, two pictures: photographs of the *Discobolus* and the Hermes of Praxiteles, which, because of their subjects' sex and their lack of any attempt to conceal it, have led to some doubts on the subject of Miss Martin's morals: it is felt that a print of The Soul's Awakening would have been more fitting to an Instructor of Youth. Yet two years of anxious scrutiny of Miss Martin's conduct have failed to reveal any partiality to men, and Mrs. Bentley, who naturally supervises her correspondence, is in a position to deny (if she chose to be indiscreet) the existence of any outside male attachment.

Miss Martin's life is as clean and airy and austere as her little sitting-room. She is a brisk, energetic young woman, with candid grey eyes and soft brown hair; and though nobody can maintain that her face is pretty—her features are undistinguished and her teeth, though perfect, irregular—her figure, which she habitually conceals under a not very well-cut navy-blue tailor-made suit and a white silk blouse open at the neck, has an air of health and freedom in which some would find beauty. She is probably more completely alive than anyone else in Monk's Norton, and undoubtedly better-read and better educated than anyone of her own age (which is twenty-eight), being a graduate in Arts of the University of North Bromwich. Her speech is certainly purer than that of the young ladies at The Grange and less affected than the Rector's or old Miss Abberley's.

In spite of these attributes, which are admitted in higher circles with patronizing surprise, Hilda Martin, because of her calling, cannot be classed as a 'lady.' Her station has been irrevocably fixed—not only by her social superiors but by the rest of the village—at the level of the farmers, the innkeeper and the better-class tradesmen. She has never, in fact, set foot in The Grange or The Manor. When she is invited to tea at the Rectory, on school or parish business, Mrs. Follows awkwardly makes it quite clear that this is a condescension. Mr. Sheldon-Smith would not dream of raising his hat to her; and though Dr. Hemming, whose useful ally she is, always treats her with courteous familiarity, his wife—who at the time when he married her was a nursing-sister—would feel herself in danger of losing caste if she invited Miss Martin (or even the district nurse) to supper and talk on a Sunday evening. Not that Miss Martin minds, or is even acutely aware of these odious distinctions. She is a shrewdly-humorous and self-contained young person.

Her life is a full one; and she knows that the 'ladies' of the village have not enough to give her to make it worth her while to waste time on the honour of their society. When she is not busy with her school-children—and her duty, as she conceives it, consists in a great deal more than pushing them up into Standard Six, being that of a friend and a sanitary missionary—she has her books, which George Mason brings on the 'bus from Worcester, her daily paper and two weekly reviews which would scare the 'ladies' stiff (if they saw them) by their political colour, and runs the 'County Library.'

In Summer she spends every moment she can snatch, out of doors, for she is an earnest field-naturalist, enjoying the fresh air that seems her appropriate element, and bringing home rare and common flowers which she shows to the children. In Winter she does most of the work, but gets little of the honour, of the Women's Institute, and teaches and conducts a little Choral Society. She is, without doubt, the most intelligent and the happiest woman in Monk's Norton. The thing she misses most in the village is music. The organ in the church is not a responsive instrument. Though two dead grands lie silent at The Manor and The Grange, it has never occurred to either of their owners to offer Miss Martin the use of them; but next year, with luck, she expects to be able to buy a cottage-piano and a gramophone, which will be much more fun than her out-of-date battery wireless set.

Next to the post office, and attached to it, stands the saddler's shop kept by Mr. Webber, a bleached, sinewy man of sixty with sad eyes and a straggling white beard. Mr. Webber's father kept the shop before him and did steady trade, no doubt, in traces and horse-collars and shining brass hames and saddles; but the petrol age, which has carried George Mason triumphantly up in the world from the state of a mere dabbler in the elementary mechanics of bicycles to that of a garage proprietor, a 'stockist' of tyres and spare-parts, and the owner of the brown bus, has

reduced poor Mr. Webber, a craftsman without a job, to the condition of a retailer of dog-leads and muzzles and purses and such leathery trifles, while the remains of the stock in whose making he took so much pride accumulate dust.

The farmers, it is true, still employ him for small repairs; but no man who is looking to buy a Fordson will throw away money on new harness; and the gentry, who used to hunt in his father's time and patronized local tradesmen, have not merely reduced their stables but buy their harness in London. The trouble, as Mr. Webber declares with a melancholy pride, is that his stuff wears too well. In all probability he is living on his father's savings, eking out that dwindling hoard with cobbling repairs to the flimsy boots and shoes which his neighbours are fools enough to buy ready-made in Worcester, and which let in water as soon as the first snow turns to slush. Even so, he finds customers are apt to complain of his charges, being too ignorant to realize that leather costs more than cardboard. Still, thanks to the honest workmanship, this new trade is reasonably constant. Through the party-wall, Mrs. Bentley can hear him hammering away at his last, singing hymns in a resonant bass voice whose volume seems out of proportion to the skinny Adam's-apple in which it is produced. Mr. Webber never sings anything but hymns; for his mind has a religious cast that helps to console him, no doubt, for his languishing fortunes. In religion he is a stout nonconformist and in politics an old-fashioned Liberal. The leonine heads of Gladstone and Spurgeon throw challenging glances from the walls of his work-shop. On Sundays, since there is no chapel in Monk's Norton, he and his wife trudge for miles over the fields, wet or fine, to Grafton Lovett, or King's Lench, or even Chaddesbourne, to worship (if not to preach) at one of his sect's conventicles. A knitted red woollen comforter protects him from cold, an enormous umbrella from rain. Mrs. Webber, a silent woman, with blond hair of the type that never goes grey and a flat, pale face, goes with him wherever he goes. They have had only one child, a boy, who forsook the chapel and went to the bad; served a sentence for obtaining money by false pretences and then emigrated to Canada, and was heard no more of. Since his conviction, his father has never mentioned his name. Yet the tragedy is Mrs. Webber's rather than his. Her mind is divided between hopes that her boy will return and fear of her husband's attitude if he should. For the heart of this upright man is adamant.

Between Mr. Webber's decadent saddlery and George Mason's garage, which is the last as well as the latest commercial establishment on the main street, lie Harry Hawley's butcher's shop, with its yard and slaughterhouse at the back, and *the* shop (as it is always called) of Mr. Cantlow. Harry Hawley is probably the most prosperous tradesman as well as the most highly-coloured personality in Monk's Norton. He is the only son of a small farmer in the north of the county, who made money during the war years. Harry himself was just old enough, at that time, to get into khaki, and too young to reach the front. Even at that age he was sufficiently shrewd to realize that the good days of farming would soon be over; that people must always eat meat, and that the retailer of meat takes less risk and makes more profit than the producer. When his father died, just before the end of the boom, Harry sold out the property, lock, stock and barrel, married a wife who had come into a little money of her own, and set up on the proceeds as a country butcher.

He is only thirty-six years of age, but looks ten years older: a clean-shaven, red-faced man, with long yellow teeth and keen, humorous blue eyes which can suddenly glow with anger or harden to steel. Though his figure has coarsened, he still has the carriage of an athlete, and his long thin legs in their cord riding-breeches have a sinewy look. His smiling face, his bluff, downright speech and his ringing laugh are familiar not only in Monk's Norton but in every market-town within twenty miles of it, and in the hunting-field too, for he likes to feel himself a cut above the ordinary, unenterprising tradesmen, and to mix with his betters on the common ground of sport. Among these and others who only know him slightly, he passes as a careless, good-natured, happy-go-lucky fool. But Harry Hawley is no fool. There is no shrewder judge of a beast or a horse between North Bromwich and Worcester. All is grist that comes to the mill of his lively commercial intelligence. He has a nose for an opportunity, and can pick up a profit in affairs where duller minds can only see loss. There is nothing—land, horses, fruit-crops—that he is not ready to buy and sell. Even his gambles—and he is an inveterate gambler—generally come off. No other man could neglect his legitimate business as he does and still remain solvent, and folk who had prophesied for him a disastrous ending, continue to be disappointed. The fellow has the devil's own luck, they say, and leave it at that.

He is certainly lucky in his wife, who looks after the shop while Hawley goes dashing about the countryside on his restless business. It is one of the major mysteries of life at Monk's Norton that a woman so different from him in every respect as Mrs. Hawley should have chosen a man of that type for a husband, and have remained happily married to him for the last fifteen years. She is as modest as he is flamboyant, as delicate as he is coarse: a small woman, elegantly made, with a pure, pale face, a mouth which always wears an expression of unusual sweetness, quiet eyes, of an almost childlike innocence, and extraordinarily beautiful, white hands. It gives one something of a shock to see those refined fingers of hers handling the joints and fragments of raw flesh with which it is her lot to deal. You notice how she instinctively wipes them as soon as she has served you; yet there is no trace of disgust to be seen on her quiet face. Though she talks very little (her voice is as gentle as her movements) there is more 'in her' than would appear. Without her husband's commercial *flair*, she is a capable business woman. Mr. Hawley's are the only books in Monk's Norton that are kept by double entry, and the only bills that never show a mistake.

It is possible, of course, as people who pity her suggest, that Mrs. Hawley's serenity conceals a profound unhappiness; that she is, in fact, an exceptionally proud and courageous woman making the best of a very bad job. However cleverly she may pretend, she must surely realize her husband's grossness; she must know that he spends most of his evenings drinking at the inn and, once a week on an average, is the worse for whisky; that his speculations are perilous and that his gambling may land them in Queer Street; that he is often unfaithful to her (anxious mothers hesitate before letting their girls go "into service" at the Hawleys' house) and that one illegitimate child at least has been put to his reckoning. She may know all these things; yet she also knows that Harry, whatever his faults may be, adores her and needs her and counts on her. To her he remains the dashing lover of her girlhood, with whom, quite possibly, she is still a little in love. Whatever defects he may have as a husband have been there ever since first she knew him; while his virtues as a father have now become more important.

Their two children, indeed, a boy and a girl of thirteen and fourteen, are the centre of both their lives. It is to their benefit that all Hawley's shrewdness and skill are directed. He even gambles for them. "I've just put a fiver on the two-thirty for our Tommy," he will say; and the money that follows his proverbial luck goes into her pocket. Their business premises, all the odd bits of land he has acquired and every penny of their profits and savings, stand in her name. "If I took a toss and broke my neck or went bankrupt," he says, "you and the kids 'll be all right anyway, Ethel, and nobody can touch what you've got."

Perhaps it is this common devotion that accounts, more than anything else, for their solidarity. Until now Harry Hawley's luck has served him so well that the two children have enjoyed a better education than either of their parents. The girl, who is delicate, has been sent to an expensive school on the south coast, and the boy, who has something of his father's physique (on which twenty years of hard living have made very little impression) is doing well—particularly at games—at a minor public school in Gloucestershire. "The best is good enough for my kids," Harry Hawley boasts, "and so long as I've got the cash, it's the best they're going to have, you make no mistake!" So Mrs. Hawley puts by the money and pays their school fees and serves meat in the butcher's shop with her delicate hands and tries, when they are at home, to prevent their father from spoiling them and from letting them see him when he is market-peart.

Mr. Cantlow (his first name is Jabez) who keeps "the shop" next door to the Hawleys, is a person as different from his neighbour as one could well imagine. The shop has been kept by the Cantlows for three generations, and the family has inhabited Monk's Norton for eight or nine. There is nothing flashy or adventurous about Jabez Cantlow: no betting, no by-blows, no shady associations or dubious ambitions. Mr. Cantlow has never made a decision in his life without sleeping on it, and is proud of his reputation for sobriety and level-headedness. He is a small, narrow-headed man of fifty-seven, with thin dark greasy hair and a drooping moustache, neither of which, as yet, shows the least sign of turning grey. His small eyes are set close together, and are narrowed behind steel-rimmed spectacles. On week-days he wears a dark alpaca overall, on Sundays, as the People's Churchwarden, he goes to church in a frock-coat and a bowler hat. His manner, towards strangers and his social betters, is ingratiating: to these he gives the impression of being a steady, obliging, superior man. Towards his staff, which consists of an unmarried daughter of thirty-three and a hobbledehoy who spends his life running errands and opening packing-cases, and in the bosom of his family, he is an irritable tyrant.

The shop, the largest commercial establishment in the village, is divided by a central elongated island of boxes containing limp oranges and Spanish onions and eggs and vegetables, into two sides: one devoted to groceries and the other to miscellaneous ironmongery, hosiery, Manchester goods and drapery. There is hardly anything essential to life in the country, from hay-forks and patent churns to bass brooms and toothcombs, from bacon and self-raising flour to Epsom salts, that cannot be raked up from the recesses of Mr. Cantlow's shop or from the store at the back: he prides himself, indeed, on the comprehensiveness of his stock, though there is also nothing that cannot be bought at least ten per cent cheaper and better in Worcester.

The gentry, who have their own means of conveyance, have long since discovered this. They complain of his prices and only use him as a convenience in case of emergency. Mr. Cantlow, though he treats them with respect, can do without them. He prefers to deal with the cottage-folk, who live from hand to mouth, who can only find cash for the necessaries of life on Saturdays, and are thankful to pay through the nose so long as he gives them credit. Mr. Cantlow conveniently buys their surplus eggs and the fruit from their gardens; Mr. Cantlow will oblige with a short-term loan if they are pressed for the rent; Mr. Cantlow rejoices in a running account: with the result that three-quarters of the householders of Monk's Norton are in his debt, struggling, like bewildered flies, in the net of his fine-ruled ledgers and spidery handwriting, while Mr. Cantlow himself is not merely able to pose as a public benefactor and command more deference than the squire, the parson or the doctor, but also to buy what he wants at a price that suits him, and to exert those private pressures and secret threats which are as the breath of life to his scheming nature. That is why, every year at the Parish Meeting, he is re-elected People's Churchwarden and Chairman of the Council. That is why, beginning where his father left off, he has gradually acquired the cottages (in scandalous disrepair) and odd parcels of land which make him, after Mr. Sheldon-Smith, the largest landowner in Monk's Norton, and its most powerful inhabitant. And the reason why he hates his next-door neighbour, Harry Hawley, and longs to queer his pitch, is not, as he lets it be thought, because Harry is a lecher, a drinker and a gambler and no communicant, but simply because Harry's nature is open and generous and because, more than once, he has rescued an unfortunate labourer from the ledger's net. In spite of all this, Jabez Cantlow appears the most respectable, if not the most respected member of the village community. All the powers that be defer to his unquestioned solidity and flatter his pride. When he dies, no doubt, he will have an impressive funeral and be buried, in the odour of sanctity, under a granite slab inscribed with a catalogue of virtues.

DOWN THE ROAD

II

Down the Road

BEYOND the collection of business premises at the Cross and George Mason's garage—an impudent eruption of galvanized iron beset by metallic debris, which is the only symptom of the machine-age visible in Monk's Norton—the village street, dipping gently downhill, assumes those aspects of the obvious picturesque which colour the dreams of exiles. The Wessex-born Addison knew what he was about when, searching for the setting most typical of English country life, he placed Sir Roger de Coverley's domain in these parts. In the middle of the county, where rolling tawny marls cover a hundred square miles, you may find, as you twist through a maze of lanes that baffle all sense of direction, a dozen humble villages resembling yet different from Monk's Norton. The reason for their variety lies, perhaps, in the lack of a workable freestone in which (as in the neighbouring Cotswold) a style might be fixed, and in the builders' reliance on clay and oak and thatch: materials which are not only softer in texture and more amenable to improvisations but also suggestive of a less rigid existence than that to which men must brace themselves on wind-swept uplands.

This rustic architecture is one that can only flourish on lands rich in timber. When the earliest of the Monk's Norton cottages were built, Arden still was green, and a squirrel could cross two counties by leaping from bough to bough. Even now, though the glades of great trees have vanished, the depth of the soil is so great, its nature so fruitful, and the Atlantic air that ebbs and flows over the Severn basin is so bland, that these villages, set within orchards and gardens, still wear a woodland air. Their gentle shapes and hues do no violence to the surrounding greenness, adopting, indeed, in their dapplings of rusty lichen and clambering ivy and mossy thatch, a sort of protective colouring that makes them appear a natural part of it.

The irregular line of cottages, each different from its neighbour, which prolongs the main street of Monk's Norton to the gates of The Grange, occupies only one side of the road, the left as you go downhill. Though the road falls gradually, the bank on which they are built maintains its level, so that all of them—if the struggling fruit-trees of their front gardens would permit it, and if the buildings themselves did not huddle so closely to the soil—would look out, from this mild elevation, over billows of green fields and dark spinney, to a blue line of distant hills: the stark serrations of the Malverns and their more wooded northern prolongations, and, even more distant, the filmy shapes of the Clees. Between the road and the bank on which the cottages stand runs a ditch, clogged in summer with lush grasses and horse-mint, which holds in winter a permanent trickle of water and becomes, at last, a tributary of the Brandon Brook. It is so deep and so wide that here and there it is spanned for convenience by culverts and wooden bridges uniting the road and the path, which is no more than a strip of foot-trodden earth between turfy verges.

All these dwellings (or all save Ivy Cottage, the last in the row) are built with half-timber frames of black oak and roofed with straw-thatch. Some, in which the spaces between the framework are filled with plastered rubble, are whitewashed. Others,

in which the filling is of brick, have the natural hue of the material from which the soft local bricks were once made, a tawny clay which, in its fine granular texture, and in the power which its granules possess of reflecting (one might almost say of retaining) warm light, resembles the Permian sandstone of which the church tower is built.

Except in one or two of the earliest examples—hovels dating from the end of the fifteenth century whose main skeleton consists of two gigantic curved timbers that spring from the earth in which their butts are imbedded and meet under the thatch overhead in an acute-angled Gothic arch, like the ribs of an inverted ship or an arch of whalebone—the Monk's Norton half-timber is usually of a simple design: nothing more than a rectangular trellis of filled framing with diagonal cross-pieces inserted only at the angles to counter the roof's outward strain. No inventive fancy has found vent in carving or patternwork. The timber is planned to fulfil a constructive function; and since most of it has now weathered three centuries, the builders' ghosts have not very much to complain of. Indeed, Time's ravages have treated them kindly by giving a variety not only of colour but of shape—bulgings, subsidences and distortions—to buildings which, when they were new, must have appeared as aggressively rectilinear as Messrs. Astill's the brewers' glaring essays in the false antique on the outskirts of North Bromwich.

The changes of shape are due, of course, to the fact that the Monk's Norton cottages are built without adequate foundations. The great vertical studs of framework were erected on blocks of sandstone, the cross-pieces pegged to them, the spaces between filled with rubble or brick, and the stiff clay beaten until it grew hard as stone to form a floor, which, in later days, more for the sake of cleanliness than for that of appearance, was overlaid with slabs of slate and shale. As time went on, while some vertical studs stood firm, others, grounded more softly, sank beneath the weight they sustained. Many cross-pieces warped and sagged of themselves or were wrenched and twisted out of line by lateral strains. Sometimes rain, seeping in through a hole in neglected thatch, or moisture sucked up by capillary fissures from the ground, permeated the squares of rubble till they perished and crumbled, and rotted the casement-frames and threw doorposts out of plumb. There is no end to the number of defects which at various times in three hundred years have been discovered, patched-up and concealed by a smear of plaster or a dab of whitewash on those patient walls, with the result that to-day there is no such thing as a straight line in their whole composition and that they resemble the work of a freakish draughtsman rather than that of an engineer. If Fred Perry, who has no use for the picturesque, had his way, he would demolish the lot and set up in their place a row of "council houses" every one the dead spit of its neighbour, with four-inch brick walls and imported deal sash-windows and blue slate roofs. Jabez Cantlow is shocked at such an idea—not (as he pretends) out of any æsthetic fervour, but because three of the old cottages belong to him; and Miss Abberley, who owns the remainder, is on Mr. Cantlow's side because, if the cottages were pulled down, it would "spoil the village."

Fred Perry, unfortunately, for once in a way is right. In the seventeenth century, when they were new, the black-and-white cottages may not have fallen far below the standard of sanitation and comfort allotted to a brutish and ignorant peasantry. In the nineteenth, when urban conditions were even more degrading, and whole cities were improvised out of noisome and verminous back-to-backs, they might just have been tolerated. In the twentieth their romantic picturesqueness does not excuse them: they are a social disgrace. Not one of them has room for a bath or what is politely called "indoor sanitation." Their domestic water-supply must be drawn laboriously, bucket by bucket, from shallow wells the purity of which is not above suspicion. Their thatched roofs, if they do not leak, become, in winter, half-sodden sponges of rotting straw exhaling odours of mildew, while the slate-slabbed floors which are laid upon clammy clay are always cold and darkened here and there by patches of damp which show where water is lying. The treads of the stairs and the floors of the rooms upstairs are worn into holes and warped to disclose crevasses with rat-gnawed edges. Ventilation they have in plenty, for no door fits and no window is watertight, though the chinks in the casements and frames are stuffed with brown paper; but the sanitary virtue of airiness (if perpetual draughts deserve that euphemism) is heavily overbalanced by the dungeon darkness to which their inmates are condemned not merely by the inadequate window-space of their small-paned lattices but by the shadow of the dripping thatch, the festoons of clambering greenery that envelop them, and the pallid pot-plants set to catch the sun on the sills. There are corners in those low-ceiled living-rooms and in the dank lean-to sculleries that no direct light save that of lamp or candle has ever illuminated.

During the only season in which adventurous strangers exploring the countryside are likely to discover them, the black-and-white cottages "down the road" do not reveal their defects. It is natural and easy enough to find life idyllic when April enchants the mossy paths with clumps of polyanthus and gilly-flowers and pale-spiked daffodils, and the bare boughs of plum-trees, smooth and dusky as gun-metal, are sprayed with flurries of living snow: easier still in June, when lazy cuckoos are calling, when the apple-blow falls petal by petal on growing grass, and cider-fruit is setting amid clusters of pale green leaf. At this season, indeed, the very daylight seems loth to leave the sky; the air is so kind and the sense of lush growth and soft abandonment in every live thing so persuasive that the mere state of living becomes endowed with a peculiar, wistful sweetness; and where could one's days be more placidly spent, the stranger asks himself, than in these humble dwellings where life demands so little: no more than cool shade from the glistering sun by day and at evening the peace of that drowsy enveloping greenness whose perfume pervades the warm air and softens the heart? And what content could be richer than that of the first days of autumn, when the last of the tasselled fruit has been stripped from plum-tree boughs that sweep the ground with the weight of their burden, when worm-eaten apples pitch with a sudden plop into the dewy grass where greedy wasps gorge themselves on the rotten pulp, and red-barred admiral butterflies, drunk with sweet cider, spread their velvet fans? Now from every potato-patch, lately rank with green growth, the crop, which is the mainstay of life, has been lifted and the yellow haulms lie withered in rows that disclose the tawny soil. Gold reddens the leaves of the perry-pears and flaws the heavier green of the elms in patches; the very air and the dancing gnats are golden; and the level rays of this mild equinoctial sunshine give a penetrating warmth peculiarly grateful to aged bones. It is a radiance which brings old men tottering to the garden-gate, where they stand with their backs to the sun and let it soak through while the smoke goes up straight from the thatch. The air is so still that their slow speech has the strange clarity of sounds heard on frosty mornings; so thin and so clear that they can catch the drone of the threshing-machine at Goodrest Farm. They stand there and talk, and watch their sons who are trenching the baked garden plots in readiness for the autumn planting. Bees pillage the pollen of their late harvest in the Michaelmas daisies. The sun goes down huge and red into a layer of mist which settles on the cooling earth; its last rays enrich the opulent hues of the heavy-headed dahlias. The old men shiver and crawl back to their draughty ingles. There is a promise of frost in the night. To-morrow morning the dahlia-heads may hang limp and blackened; and after that they know there will be five months of winter, and perhaps, for them, no new spring.

It is something, after all, that these ancients have come to be as old as they are. They come of a sturdy stock, their constitutions toughened by generations of hardship and unsapped, heaven knows, by luxurious living. The people who inhabit these cottages are a long-lived race. The ills which cripple and kill them, Dr. Hemming will tell you, are mainly those which are due to exposure and damp: rheumatic diseases of joints and nerves and muscles and bronchitic infections, recurring each winter until they come once too often. They are a prolific race (or have been till lately) with plenty of stalwart sons and buxom daughters, brought up, in a not very distant past, on a labourer's wage of less than a pound a week, who work on the land and "go into service" as soon as they are old enough to fend for themselves. They are poor folk. In not one of those cottages "down the road" is there a man who earns more than forty shillings a week. And even that is precarious, depending not merely on health but on the fortunes and sometimes the caprices of his employer. They are essentially a respectable race. Very few ever get into troubles more serious than the results of riding bicycles on footpaths or without a light, the offences that P.C. Homes has most often to deal with. They have a strict sense of duty. It is part of the young people's acknowledged debt to contribute to their parents' living as soon as they come to need it. Daughters-in-law are sometimes a little jealous; but tradition in this matter is usually stronger than Scripture, and few parents with sons in good jobs want as long as they live. They are a capable race. Though most of them would be described on a census-paper as "unskilled labourers," their labour is very different from that of the better-paid workers, themselves machines, who tend machines in factories. They are masters of many complicated and exquisite crafts—land-drainage, shepherding, forestry, hedge-laying, thatching, ploughing—and the repository of much knowledge, part traditional and part acquired by experience and acute observation, of the vagaries of nature. They know the peculiarities of the land on which they work: how one pasture is sour and another kind, how it lies to wind and to water. They are skilled in the habits and handling of stock, knowing which crosses succeed and which invite failure and what feeding, in given cases, gives good results and what leads to disaster. They are experts in weather, and can read the face of the sky with as little margin of error as a wireless weather-forecast. In the handling of the soil and the things that grow in it, their calloused fingers have a fine delicacy, like that of a surgeon's. And not only are they expert in these crafts; they are also (and reasonably) proud of the skill that can drive a straight furrow over uneven land, or insert a graft that will grow like a natural break in the bark of a plum or apple tree, or shear an awkward sheep without drawing blood, or fell a tree to lie as it should, or geld a bullock. There is no such thing in Monk's Norton as an unskilled farm-labourer.

They are, moreover, an ancient race, with elements in their

lineage that may account more than a little for their pride and their decency, having not been sufficiently in-bred to produce degeneracy. The names they go by, distorted by ignorant phonetics, are not merely, in different versions, engraved on the ancient tombstones and memorials of the parish church. Many, prevalent still, have their place in Domesday, and some are recorded in history. There are Norman Pipards and Foliots and Laceys and Verdons, and Saxon Mucklows and Lydiatts. Mr. Jagger, who lives at Ivy Cottage, at the end of the row, is our authority on these and all other matters of history. Mr. Jagger maintains that old Joe Shelton, the thatcher, has far more of the authentic Sheldon blood in his veins than Mr. Sheldon-Smith, and more right to the Sheldon bearings—*Sable, a fesse, between three sheldrakes argent*—which are carved so arrogantly (and improperly) above the porch of The Grange.

Ivy Cottage, where Mr. Jagger lives, lies a little nearer the Grange than the last of the black and white cottages. He is what geologists would call "intrusive" in the Triassic horizon, not having been born in Monk's Norton but having, to all intents and purposes, become part of its texture. He has lived at Ivy Cottage for rather more than nine years, and the excitement and curiosity originally excited by his purchasing it are just beginning to die down; for though the old folks who live "down the road" still regard him with the suspicion proper to a foreigner, and shake their heads as they ask what made him leave his "native," the young married people have been aware of him since they were at school, and their children, having never seen it without him, accept his presence as a natural feature in the landscape.

Indeed, if any urban alien has earned the right to naturalization in Monk's Norton it is Mr. Jagger. He entered the village for the first time, by sheer accident, nearly thirty years before he settled in it. He came on a cushion-tyred bicycle, and dismounted for tea, with damson jam, at the "Sheldon Arms," then kept by Amos Perry, Fred Perry's father. It was on an April evening; then, too, a cuckoo had been calling from the elms in the field called The Cubbs at the back of the inn. Mr. Jagger—a spry young business-man, with handsome moustaches, tight knickerbockers, and a pleated Norfolk jacket buttoned up to the level of an exceedingly high starched collar—had stepped out, after tea, into a world that seemed drenched with enchantment. Though the trees were but lightly fledged, the orchards stood dusted with plum-blossom. The whole delicate scene was sketched in black and white with a wash of tenderest green that gave it an air of freshness and innocence, and the evening silence released such a torrent of birdsong as he had never heard before. Mr. Jagger, refreshed and stimulated by his tea, left his bicycle at the inn door and explored the whole village on foot—from the white gate where straggling yew-hedges concealed the Grange's gentility to the sandstone bridge, spanning the brook, over which he had arrived; from the watersplash, which complicated a cyclist's approach from the east, to the line of the "cut" which was completely impassable. At the end of these explorations he visited the church. The porch-gate was padlocked—it was unusual in those days for anyone to enter the building except on Sundays—but the graveyard was full of old tombstones whose carven inscriptions were in tune with this bland, elegiac evening mood.

Idly scrutinizing these, with the mild sentimental detachment of a man in vigorous health and at peace with the world, he was brought up with a jolt by deciphering, on one of the oldest, his own name. *Here lyes the body*, he read, *of Ambrose Jagger*, *Farmer*, *of this Parish*, 83 *years of age*. The tombstone dated from the end of the eighteenth century: this Ambrose Jagger, he calculated, must have been born in the age of Queen Anne. From that moment his attitude, if still sentimental, was no longer detached. He sat there, in bemused reflection, till the flood of birdsong ebbed and the rooks came cawing home from their distant pastures. As he left the churchyard he felt at once awed and elated. He had a feeling that even if he had no part in those buried bones (and the coincidence of both names was remarkable) he had at least discovered a spiritual ancestor. He decided that if it were possible, he would certainly stay the night at the "Sheldon Arms."

It was possible, though somewhat unusual. Mr. Perry confessed that he was not in the habit of catering for tourists. The visitor, in fact, was the first example of the species he had ever encountered: not unnaturally, since the road that entered Monk's Norton led nowhere in particular, and apart from a few of "them there cyclists," who poked in everywhere nowadays, strange faces were rarely seen.

That night Mr. Jagger sat unobtrusively sipping sharp cider, which was treacherously potent, and listening to the slow talk of Mr. Perry's customers in the bar. They were most of them older than himself, and, one and all, covered with a shaggy rustic patina, like lichen on weathered tree-trunks. The matter of their discourse was trivial, and their speech, at times, unintelligible; yet, in spite of these drawbacks, Mr. Jagger experienced a burning though vain desire to be admitted to this exclusive society. The evening was well advanced before he plucked up courage to ask if any of his relatives, of the name of Jagger, remained in Monk's Norton.

"Jagger? Jagger?" the cronies repeated. They scratched their heads and wagged them emphatically, deciding that nobody of that name or anything like it had ever been heard on there or thereabouts.

Mr. Jagger enlightened them with enthusiastic details of the birth and death of his newly-acquired spiritual ancestor. Even these were received with caution. The sexton himself had never noticed the tombstone, though he was prepared, with polite reservations, to admit its existence.

"It's there all right," Mr. Jagger informed them proudly, "and my name's Ambrose Jagger too."

"If that's so," the eldest of the party declared judicially, "I reckon as this here gentleman has the right to count himself a Monk's Norton man."

They laughed, dismissing the fantastic claim as a joke; but to Mr. Jagger it was neither a joke nor fantastic. Up till then this timid and lonely little man had never experienced a sentimental attachment. From that moment his existence became dominated by one fierce desire: to enforce the shadowy claim and to identify himself with the past, the present, and such future as he might share with Monk's Norton. All his Hackney evenings were spent in bookish researches into its geography, geology and history. So often as he could free himself from his clerkly employment—on every Bank Holiday and during his annual fortnight's vacation—he would push out his ancient bicycle and ride north-west into Worcestershire. In this manner he grew, by degrees, to be a familiar figure; a harbinger, like the cuckoos and swallows, of changing seasons. From "that there cyclist chap" he became "the gent from London," and, at last, "Mr. Jagger." Eyes that once had regarded him with grudging surprise began to betray recognition and friendliness; nods welcomed him, and then smiles, and, finally, words.

"Well, well, sir, how be you? I was only a'saying to our Bob the other night: 'It'll be just about time for Mr. Jagger to be coming along again.'"

Yet it was no less than fifteen years after he first set eyes on Ivy Cottage that Mr. Jagger, arriving on his summer holiday, remarked the notice-board announcing that it was for sale. With this discovery a new and at first sight fantastic ambition entered his life. Up till now he had merely been possessed by the village: if he bought Ivy Cottage and the minute plot of ground on which it stood, he might count himself a possessor as well as possessed. No doubt the property would cost far more than he could command; yet the wild idea kept him awake as he tossed through that summer night in the trough of old Mr. Perry's best feather-bed. Next morning he broached the subject timidly.

"Ivy Cottage? Ay, poor Mrs. Tolley's gone," the landlord said, "and her daughter-in-law, she wants to sell it, I'm told. If so be as anyone took a fancy to it, like, they might let it go for two or three hundred pounds. Mr. Collins up at the Goodrest, he has the handling of it; but I'm told Mr. Sheldon-Smith has got his eye on it for the under-gardener."

An anxiety akin to terror fell on Mr. Jagger's mind. What, last night, had seemed a rash, intoxicating aspiration, became an urgent desire. He bolted his breakfast, scalding his mouth with hot tea, and pedalled away with trembling legs through the watersplash to The Goodrest. The news that Mr. Sheldon-Smith had his eye on the cottage dispelled his last shred of caution. He ran Mr. Collins to earth looking over his lambs in the field called Long Dragon Piece. He panted:

"I've come about Ivy Cottage."

"What's up? Not a fire?"

"No. I've heard it's for sale, and I want to buy it," Mr. Jagger said.

Mr. Collins burst out laughing. "If that's all," he said, "you can have the place and welcome for two hundred and fifty . . . cash down, mind. It's as good as a gift."

Two hundred and fifty pounds. . . . It was approximately the total, at that moment, of Mr. Jagger's savings, to the last penny he had scraped together during his working life. If he spent it, there would be nothing left between him and destitution, no line of retreat on which to fall back in case of disaster. The decision he made was, according to scale, heroic.

"Two hundred and fifty. Very well: I'll take it," he said.

Ivy Cottage is not, by Monk's Norton standards, beautiful. It was built in the eighteen-eighties, by the Sheldon-Smiths' predecessors at The Grange, in the very worst style of Victorian neo-gothic, with a high-pitched slate roof and small mullioned windows recklessly glazed with coloured glass. The parasite which gives it its name has mercifully obscured its architectural defects; and the style, after all, is in keeping with Mr. Jagger's mediæval mind. On his retirement he came to end his days in it. He is no longer the spry young commercial gentleman with the handsome moustache who "discovered" Monk's Norton thirty years ago, though he still wears tight knickerbockers and a Norfolk jacket buttoned up to a high starched collar, and still rides a bicycle. He is, in fact, a rather seedy old man, with weak red-rimmed eyes and a wispy moustache. Yet his passion has never failed him. Monk's Norton, and everything that pertains to it—particularly to its past—remains the absorbing interest of his life. The subject, which he has made his own, is inexhaustible, and the carefully-docketed papers over which he broods for so many lamp-lit hours are concerned not merely with the place's documentary history but with personal observations of such contemporary matters as records of rainfall and temperature and relative humidity; of the dates on which migrant birds arrive and are heard and depart and of their nesting-habits; of the appearance of such rare and irregular visitants as crossbills and comma butterflies and (just once) a golden oriole. Since he came to live in Monk's Norton, his range has widened. There is not a church within ten miles about which he does not know more than its incumbent. He writes letters to the local papers announcing the rareties he discovers, and correcting the loose conclusions of other local archæologists. His life is completely solitary. How he contrives to exist on his minute savings remains a mystery. No doubt he receives a good many presents of perishable produce—an occasional basket of eggs or fruit, a sack of potatoes, or a barrel of cider—for most Monk's Norton people, though the village accepted him so tardily, are now proud of his erudition, and think of him as a "character." Others, including Major Sheldon-Smith, speak of him as a crank.

THEIR BETTERS

III

Their Betters

IT would be unfair to Mr. Sheldon-Smith to attribute his depreciation of Mr. Jagger to the circumstance that through his own dilatoriness (or Mr. Jagger's rash precipitancy) he failed to acquire Ivy Cottage for his under-gardener, or to that difference of opinion about old Shelton the thatcher's right to bear the fesse and the argent sheldrakes, or even to the fact that Mr. Jagger knows so much more about "his village" (as he usually calls it) than he does. Monk's Norton is only his village in so far as his grandfather, Sir Josiah Smith (the hyphen came later), a Wednesford colliery-owner and ironmaster, purchased the Lordship of the Manor and rebuilt The Grange in the year of Queen Victoria's first jubilee. After all, a tenure of three generations is not bad in these days, and Major Sheldon-Smith, having been educated at Eton, is happily immune from subconscious sensations of inferiority. By the "County," which is itself an increasingly elastic society, apart from such rigid champions of lost causes as the Abberleys and Ombersleys and d'Abitots, to whom Burke's Landed Gentry means nothing, and who pretend not to look down their noses at anyone whose name doesn't appear in Domesday or Dugdale's Monastica or the Visitation of Worcestershire, his position is accepted without question. He is a deputy lieutenant, and a member of the Hunt Club and all that, and in most other things a citizen of high repute. Yet somehow, as long as that old cat Annabel Abberley lives at The Manor—merely continues to exist there—he knows that he can never be the most important person in Monk's Norton.

Not that this worries him much—except through his wife, whom it worries a good deal. Major Sheldon-Smith has, in fact, quite enough to worry about without considering matters of social precedence. Though he isn't precisely hard-up, he is six or seven hundred pounds a year poorer than his circumstances require. That is partly the fault of his grandfather, who was in too great a hurry to found a family and set up as a country gentleman, retiring from active business with a fortune just a little too small and overspending himself on the reconstruction of the Manor House: even more the fault of his father, who, brought up in a softer school, had not the energy to rouse himself to face the decline of the heavy industries and adapt himself to it, but took fright and sold out of the family business at the bottom of the slump, thus marking another step in the cycle of three generations which is traditionally required to carry an industrial family from clogs to clogs. It is also, more than a little, the fault of Mr. Sheldon-Smith himself; a pleasant-spoken, but rather slovenly man, quite incapable of doing anything to his declining fortunes but grumble about them.

The only real job of work he has ever done was commanding a labour battalion during the war. He farms on a fairly large scale, but leaves everything to his bailiff, and has never taken the trouble to master the principles of the business or realized that farming is now something more than a gentleman's hobby. He hunts a little, not because he understands horses or hound-work, but because he knows *Jorrocks* by heart, and hunting is part of the life into which he has been born. He sits regularly and conscientiously on the bench. At election-times he becomes galvanized into an officious activity; in the intervals between them he grumbles but is politically lazy. He dutifully reads the *Morning Post*, the *Spectator* (which, lately, puzzles him), *Punch*, and the *Field*, and, occasionally, a volume of history, political memoirs or travel. As a citizen his contribution to the life of the community is not important. He is, in short, an obstinate, sober, well-meaning, rather stupid man: a typical by-product (or end-product?) of the industrial revolution; a type that is due, in the nature of things (unless some surprising "sport" evolves itself), to disappear during the next hundred years.

It is poetically just that Major Sheldon-Smith should live in a house like Monk's Norton Grange. In the days before his unhyphenated grandfather got hold of it, The Grange must have been a pleasant, half-timbered seventeenth-century building, without any particular distinction but with a style of its own, encircled by a spring-fed moat which discharged its water through a series of stagnant stew-ponds into the Brandon Brook. The first thing Sir Josiah did when he bought The Grange was to fill up the moat, which was supposed to make the house damp and breed rheumatism. As a matter of fact it was the only thing which kept the foundations dry, by acting as a drain, and was no sooner filled in than the spring broke out in the cellars. But in any case, though he liked the dignified name of the house and its surroundings (the rookery elms of the broken avenue were superb, as was the lime in which the first cuckoo sang, which rose to a height of ninety feet to the east of it), the building itself which had been occupied as a farm-house, was too small for the father of a Victorian family, and too unimpressive for the possessor of a brand-new knighthood.

So the seventeenth-century house, with its watery cellars, was left standing as a tail, and to the front of it (by no means regardless of expense, for Sir Josiah knew all about the value of money) was attached an imposing structure of lavish Victorian Tudor, with large plate-glass sash-windows in stone-cased bays, and a great deal of other ornamental freestone in the shape of gable-decorations and balustrades, and the orielled porch on which, out of compliment to his client's wife, whose maiden name had been Sheldon, the architect (who was much patronized by black-country magnates and knew their weaknesses) affixed the armorial bearings of the Monk's Norton Sheldons, fortunately extinct.

What the new Grange must have looked like when first it was built, when the freshly-cut freestone and fiery brick combined to give it the effect of a scarlet uniform with white facings, one shudders to imagine. But Time, which deals kindly with most works of man in Monk's Norton, has been generous to The Grange. Romantic ivy and vigorous Virginia creeper have so completely obscured the architect's detail (save the fesse and the three sheldrakes which are kept clear) that, apart from the huge unmullioned sash-windows, the exterior might really be Tudor. Inside it, of course, the extent of the fake becomes instantly apparent in the variegated tiling of the hall, the varnished staircase of beery pitch-pine, and the badly-proportioned panelling of the same material with which the library and dining-room are lined. The bulk of the furniture dates from a period a little earlier than the house, having been bought to adorn Sir Josiah's premises in Wednesford. It is of massive mahogany and has, at least, the virtue of honest workmanship and of not pretending, like its setting, to be what it isn't. Most of the curtains, carpets and other fabrics show the taste of the present Mrs. Sheldon-Smith, who is all for brightness, and, urged by her daughters, would like to be modern if she dared. On the whole

the furniture, though ugly, is not uncomfortable. The house has the air of being lived in; it smells strongly of flowers, which are arranged with a certain opulence, and, faintly, of dogs; yet such graces as it possesses are concentrated in the stable-buildings with their leaky lichened roof and harsh-striking clock, and in the remains of the original moated Grange at the back, the "tail" where the servants sleep and have their being.

There are not so many of them as there used to be. It is Mrs. Sheldon-Smith's chief grudge against modern times that, now that the staff with whom she started house-keeping have died off or retired or merely married, the young women of the village show no anxiety to snap up their places. It is not that servants are not well paid and well treated at The Grange. They have their own bedrooms, a comfortable servants' hall with a wireless-set, and the best of food; their needs and their personal desires are "considered" in everything; they have plenty of liberty. Nor can they complain that Monk's Norton is really "out of the world" now that George Mason's brown 'bus runs to Worcester three times a week. Yet unreasonably, obstinately, these light-headed creatures prefer to find work in factories or shops or, if they "go into service," places in the poky anonymous suburban houses of North Bromwich. There is no such thing in these days and in that class, Mrs. Sheldon-Smith complains, as personal loyalty. The more you do for them—the word "them" always signifies servants—the less they respect you. They come and they go at the dictates of pure caprice, and their parents confess that they can do nothing with them. No wonder people like herself are shutting up country houses and settling on the outskirts of London in service-flats! If it were not for her garden and her husband's prejudices and the unwelcome, undeniable fact that in London the name Sheldon-Smith counts for nothing, she would gladly abandon Monk's Norton to-morrow. So the unequal struggle goes on. For two-thirds of the year The Grange is under-staffed, its inmates living in a state of domestic emergency, almost literally from hand to mouth. If it were not for her daughters who, unlike the working-classes, are not ashamed to put their hands to anything, Mrs. Sheldon-Smith would have been forced long ago to throw up the sponge.

Her daughters, like the Graces (whom they do not resemble) and the witches in *Macbeth*, are three. Their ages vary between thirty-one and twenty-four—their only brother, the heir to the family's embarrassments, who separated the elder two, was killed at Gheluvelt. They are all three unmarried, and seem likely to remain so. Their tragedy is that the generation in which they might reasonably have expected to find husbands of their own kind was eliminated by the war; and the fact that they are much more class-conscious than the aristocracy seems likely to keep them single. As a matter of routine they have all been "presented," and three enormous photographs of them in court trains and feathers, which stand on the dead grand-piano in the drawing-room, serve as perpetual reminders to them of this distinction. They are so anxious, in fact, to know nobody but the right people that, in this sparsely-populated district, they hardly know anybody at all. It would be unthinkable, for instance, that any one of them should ever make friends with Miss Martin, who is much better (if less expensively) educated, and more cultured and more alive than they are.

This seems a pity; for the Miss Sheldon-Smiths are honest, pleasant, good-natured girls. If they have not inherited their mother's thin-lipped, thin-nosed distinction of feature, they are by no means bad-looking and, thanks to their simple upbringing, a trio of healthy and domestically-capable young women, to whom a little of Miss Martin's society might possibly have given the civilized interests in which their lives are deficient. Fortunately for them they are blandly unconscious of these deficiencies. The fact that they are completely ignorant of literature or music or painting, modern or ancient, that, though bred in the country, they know nothing whatever about its birds or beasts or flowers, does not distress them. Their sole intellectual exercise is the *Morning Post's* crossword puzzle, which, between them, in relays, they nearly solve every day. Though they are interested in the Wimbledon tennis championships and in Ladies' Golf, and are competent performers in both of these genteel games, their views on domestic politics and world-affairs are narrowed to what they pick up from their father's talk at the breakfast-table and what he, in his turn, picks up from the newspaper. In

Winter they hunt the fox courageously, and as assiduously as the family's possession of only two horses will allow. In Summer they play tennis—preferably mixed doubles—indefatigably. Their idea of a heaven which may quite probably never be theirs is to live the rest of their lives in a garrison-town in the society of manly young men, all officers and all gentlemen, who can dance and hunt and play polo and tennis and golf and a good hand at bridge, and look forward to a pension. They are the stuff, in short, from which the mates and mothers of Empire-builders are made; but whether their husbands will go on building the Empire or their sons help to repair it is another matter. In these grim days the supply of leisured and eligible young men in the services is dwindling. There are few to be seen near Monk's Norton except in the regimental depot and in the hunting-field. If their brother had lived, he would have brought gay parties of fellow-officers with him on leave, and their chances of making the only kind of marriage they consider possible would have been easier. As it is, the strain of unconscious anxiety is beginning to tell on them. There is something a little hard and over-eager discoverable in their forced heartiness, and in the standardized air of sporting good-fellowship which they assume when men are about. Their voices and their clothes are bolder, and their not very subtle make-up becomes less discreet.

In their calendar there are two cardinal dates: the first, the Hunt Ball, at which their father puts on, once a year, his pink coat with gilt buttons and pale blue facings; the second, Eton and Harrow, when, for two days, dressed to the nines (or as near as they can get to them), they hungrily promenade those dismal corridors below the stands at Lord's, convinced that in all that top-hatted assembly, the last by-product of the Industrial

Revolution, they are "in the swim" and can hardly set eyes on a single person whom they ought not to know.

Life has been much less kind to them, on the whole, than to their mother. Mrs. Sheldon-Smith is a tall, dry, shy woman of a type which only our race and her caste breed in quantities. Her eyes, which are of the nebulous blue of love-in-a-mist, are clearly incapable of showing a vulgar emotion. In the country she dresses in ill-fitting tailor-made tweeds, and wears no ornament save a diamond brooch in the form of a regimental badge. When she goes to "town" (which is what the Sheldon-Smiths call London) her suit is black, very well-cut, with a little lace at the neck. It sets off her shape, which is still slimmer than her daughters', and her carriage, which is more erect, and she still has elegant ankles of which she is so conscious that most of the money she grudgingly spends on clothes goes in hand-made shoes. Not even a casual observer could doubt that she is a lady and English.

Her main interest in life, apart from her husband and children, has been centred, since the death of her son, in the care of the garden, in which she works with an untiring devotion remarkable in so fragile a creature. This is the only thing in which any member of the family has found a vocation or justified existence by acquiring any precise knowledge. Mrs. Sheldon-Smith (though she will call anemones anenomes) is a genuinely expert gardener. She has an enviable knack or instinct for making all green things grow. Her borders—and even more than these her rockeries—afford her not merely a full-time occupation but the stuff of which all her dreams and aspirations are made. Her writing-table is littered with nurserymen's catalogues, which fill the rôle played in other people's lives by romantic literature. She has a passion for blue. The discovery and first flowering of *Meconopsis Baileyi* and the establishment of *Gentiana Sino-Ornata* in a sandstone trough found on one of the farms, have been among the most ecstatic experiences in her life, just as the faint trace of lime in the Monk's Norton Marls, which prevents her from succeeding with *Lithospermum Prostratum* and the African heaths and azaleas and rhododendrons, has been, to her, a far greater grief than her husband's straitened circumstances or anything else that has happened since the war.

This is not to say that she is not devoted to her family. Her belief in her husband's muddled rectitude and in her daughters' virtues and graces is almost pathetic. And, indeed when one takes the Sheldon-Smith family not at their own social valuation but for what they are, there is much more to be said for them than this examination suggests. They are perfectly dignified, decent, well-meaning people, with a strict, if unimaginative, sense of personal propriety and patriotic duty. They pay crippling taxes without over-much grumbling, and are prepared to sacrifice even more than money when the State demands it. If they are not exactly the salt of the English earth, they are part of its backbone, and contribute to the national countenance a stiff upper lip.

They are certainly worthy of a little more respect than Miss Annabel Abberley, of Monk's Norton Manor, allows them. Miss Abberley is no respecter of persons in any case. The Abberleys, together with their neighbours the Ombersleys of Chaddesbourne, had thrust their roots deep into the red marl long before the Norman d'Abitots and Pomfrets had ever been heard of, and they regard even these noble families as recent interlopers. No title or abundant wealth has ever come their way; no brilliant blossom has ever adorned their family tree; its sole virtue consists in its astonishing permanence. It resembles to-day (though, of course, it is centuries older) the stricken oak at the cross-roads to which Fred Perry objects, and Annabel Abberley is its last sere leaf.

Only a few years ago there were two Miss Abberleys. The younger, Miss Lettice, died at the respectable age of seventy-six. Miss Annabel, the elder, survived her and is eighty-two. She does not, the villagers report, "look her age," though, indeed, why should she? She is ageless and is not, like Miss Loach, of Chaddesbourne, who is slightly her senior, a "bed-lier." On the contrary, nothing but orders from Dr. Hemming, the only living soul she has been known to obey, can keep her from getting up and putting on her kid gloves for luncheon at one precisely.

She lives quite alone. On her sister's death her friends implored her to think of procuring a lady-companion. Miss Abberley wouldn't hear of it. Her only familiars—if such a word can be used in the case of a person who has never been known to permit the least familiarity—are her maid, commonly known at Monk's Norton as "Miss Abberley's Susan," a gentle old lady of seventy-five, whom she treats as a child, and her chauffeur, "Miss Abberley's Henry," formerly her coachman, who drives her out every fine afternoon, winter and summer, to take the air, in the enormous Daimler landaulette with which her enterprise startled Monk's Norton in the year nineteen hundred and eight. This machine, for which the supply of spare parts has long since been exhausted or scrapped, is a familiar yet always surprising spectacle in the Monk's Norton lanes. When she and her sister sold their carriages and bought it, they decided that it would have to last their time. And no doubt it will; for when Miss Abberley makes a decision nothing can shake it.

Her mind is still as diamond-hard and bright as her body is frail, and her tongue as ruthless, being armed with a swift, salty humour to which sting is added by her employment of outmoded turns of speech, such as "ain't" for "isn't," and an outspokenness which proper people find embarrassing, and timid ones scaring. Yet she is a generous tyrant. The three maids (not counting Susan) and the two men (not counting Henry or Sands the butler), who serve her are equally terrified of her and devoted to her. She never has "servant-troubles," like poor Mrs. Sheldon-Smith: the servants at the Manor, like the Daimler, have to last her time, and count it a privilege to be members of an establishment which is a cut above anything else in Monk's Norton, or, indeed, in the district.

It is remarkable how, even in her retirement and without any of the obvious advantages of rank and wealth, this imperious little old woman has impressed the whole neighbourhood with her personality. Though she makes no public appearance, save in the high, boxed pew in the south chapel of the church which has its own entrance, she is very much part of the village. Nothing happens in Monk's Norton or near it of which she is not aware, and in which she fails to be interested—not because she desires to interfere in the villagers' private lives, but for sheer love of omniscience, and out of the shrewd and cynical pleasure her mischievous sophisticated intelligence derives from the human comedy.

That, perhaps, is the true explanation of Miss Abberley's power: her spiritual detachment. She does not, in a sense, belong to the age in which she lives, or, for that matter, to any other. She is the sole surviving vehicle of a kind of life which has persisted in this remote part of England (and will persist just so long as she lives) ever since the first Saxon thegn acquired her name. Wars may redden the land, revolution may change its face and dynasties divide it, but the Abberleys still go on: they are so near to the soil, their roots reach so far down, that mere political accidents such as these are powerless to move them.

If Miss Annabel has spiritual affinities with any period they are with the late seventeenth or early eighteenth century. The fancy, if such it is, is encouraged by her surroundings. It would be difficult to find within a hundred miles of one another two houses more different in form or in atmosphere than The Manor and The Grange. One is conscious of the difference the moment one passes the wrought-iron gates and sets foot on Miss Abberley's drive. The change from the outer world is as much an adventure in time as in space. It is not that her garden, with its velvety sweep of lawn and its benignant Lebanon cedars, is more lovingly tended than that of The Grange. On the contrary, one misses the feeling of a naïve and passionate enthusiasm which Mrs. Sheldon-Smith lavishes on her pleasance. It would be easy to declare that one garden is Classical and the other Romantic; one formal, the other haphazard; juster perhaps to say that one resembles a Landscape and the other a Still Life. Stillness seems the most suitable word to describe its character—a stillness that persuades the intruder to go on tiptoe; yet, in spite of that stillness, there is no suggestion of mortality or even of somnolence. The Manor, one perceives, is very much alive and awake.

With a peculiar kind of life and of watchfulness. One feels it acutely on approaching the olive-green painted front-door with its scrolled broken pediment enclosing an inverted scallop. As one stands there, listening to the remote tinkle of the bell and the measured steps of Mr. Sands the butler muted by thick carpets as he advances, one is aware that no less than ten windows (to say nothing of dormers), each framed symmetrically, by damask below and glazed chintz above, are intently examining, assaying, quizzing one's presence, with the interested detachment of eyes that are ancient and wise. You feel it again when, invited with the most polished courtesy to enter the long hall's dim, lustrous quietude, you hear tinkling, silvery clock-chimes announce the passage of Time, and realise that, in spite of this delicate accuracy of record, you have actually stepped into a house where the measurement of Time is no more than a convenient convention and, in fact, doesn't really matter much more than anything else in a life whose rhythm has been established for centuries and will go on without winding or regulation until the works run down.

This impression is more remarkable because, although nothing in the house is new, neither is anything, according to Abberley standards, venerably old. There are, it is true, a few Tudor and Elizabethan portraits whose dark glances surprise one in unexpected corners; but very little of the furniture is older than the house itself or more than three times as old as Miss Abberley. Yet most of what one sees has the unquestionable validity of a work of art, and, at that, a masterpiece. The least variation in its form or colour would mar the illusion (if illusion it be) of timelessness which its owner shares.

The room in which Annabel Abberley habitually sits and receives her infrequent visitors is a little later in the period of its decoration than the rest of the house. Its five long windows, surmounted by pelmet-stages of tarnished gilt Chippendale carving and flanked by curtains of oyster-coloured brocade, look out on a wide flagged terrace and, beyond it, the southward sweep of walled garden which, at a lower level of the street, Miss Martin's sitting-room also commands. These five windows make the interior unusually light, throwing shadows on the delicate relief of its plasterwork panels, on the alabaster Adam mantelpiece, with its urns and swags and classical female figures in attitudes of repose, and on the mellow madders and faded greens of a threadbare French carpet. Miss Abberley herself sits surprisingly erect in a needlework armchair, whose back she despises to use, her feet set close together on a *petit-point* footstool. On her hands, which are folded peacefully in her lap—she is not, like Mrs. Sheldon-Smith, an automatic knitting-machine—she generally wears gloves, and, if not gloves, silk mittens. No ornament but a thin gold chain with a locket suspended from it distracts the eye from the severity of a black bodice which ends, at the neck, in a jabot or lappets of ancient lace. Old lace is one of Miss Abberley's expert devotions: the drawers in her Chippendale chests are full of it: sixteenth century Venetian needlepoint, hexagonal-meshed *point d'Argentan*, Mechlin pillow-lace borders, Irish crochet sleeves and creamy Honiton bridal-veils. Night and day alike, she wears caps of lace, and lace at her throat and wrists. And this taste of hers for a fabric so delicately meticulous, for the products of an art so rich in inventive pattern, so devoid of emotion, is significant of her attitude of mind. No ungoverned passions, one would guess, can ever have vexed the crystalline calm of that mind or flawed the composure of features which even now, in extreme old age, have the cold and clear-cut quality of carved ivory. Only her hard, imperious mouth, with its shade of perpetual mockery, and her eyes, with irises of a grey so dark that they appear to be black, which can still brighten superbly and still scorn the use of spectacles, give a hint of the proud, impetuous spirit, and betray the extraordinary force of character which have made and make Annabel Abberley, wrinkled and old, the force that she is: the proud, cynical mouth, the eyes, and then, when she speaks, her voice—which is not the voice of an aged woman, but resonant and (surprisingly) harsh. She likes—one suspects she has always liked—shocking her visitors. Perhaps this, together with a wicked wit which still makes the county (not Mrs. Sheldon-Smith's county, but hers) chuckle over her sayings, accounts for the fact that no man has dared to marry her. Though she is never vulgar, she can often be coarse, in an eighteenth-century fashion. In politics she is what she calls a Whig, with a cynic's contempt for the timidity and venality of all modern parties. Though she believes in the virtues of aristocracy, she is inclined to doubt if much of it any longer exists. She reads *The Times* daily, and scans *Berrow's Worcester Journal*, which is the oldest newspaper in England, once a week; but she buys few books and subscribes to no circulating library, and has no more interest in contemporary art or letters than the Miss Sheldon-Smiths—"those poor, plain things at The Grange," as she calls them, or "the Misses Smith." She is inclined to be hard on women.

And why, after all, should Miss Abberley be interested in the arts? From her birth she has been surrounded by works of unextravagant beauty, and has naturally taken her exquisite surroundings as a matter of course. She, herself, if it comes to that, is a work of art, regrettably irreplaceable. There will never be another Annabel Abberley. There will be no more Abberleys when the wind has blown that last frail leaf away.

COUNTRY DOCTOR

IV

Country Doctor

THAT the frail leaf continues to flutter so bravely is largely due to the wisdom and care of Miss Abberley's neighbour across the road, Dr. Hemming. He is the only person in Monk's Norton, or in the world, who has the privilege of penetrating the precincts of the Manor House by the green door in the long brick wall. He has his own key to it, and enters at will: far more often, in fact, than is strictly necessary; for though Miss Abberley boasts that she has never been sick or sorry since she caught that cold and nearly died of pneumonia at the time of the Austro-Prussian war in sixty-three, Dr. Hemming knows how frail she is, and likes, every now and then, to "pop over and see the old lady."

His visits are welcomed. Miss Abberley has always been more at home with men than with women, and there is something in the pragmatical outlook of a doctor that appeals to her own realistic nature. No romantic cobwebs infest Dr. Hemming's mind. He is as ruthless and downright, as little concerned with false modesties, as contemptuous of polite euphemisms and social pretensions as herself. Like Lady Chettam in *Middlemarch*, she thinks it a pity for medical men to be well-connected. Dr. Hemming is not well-connected, nor even, to judge by his speech, what the Miss Sheldon-Smiths would call a gentleman. He is a typical product of the North Bromwich Medical School, which is one of the best and most ancient in

England, and of the middle-class, from which its students are generally drawn.

He settled in Monk's Norton at the age of forty, immediately after the war in which he had served with sufficient distinction to achieve the command of a Field Ambulance and a D.S.O. He is a tallish, burly man, with a rumbling voice, fine, shrewd, grey eyes, a firm mouth, too large to be handsome, and craggy features. He wears a stiff military moustache, which makes him look more like a soldier than Major Sheldon-Smith; and his general air of rusticity is enhanced by his habit of wearing shaggy tweeds. After his eyes, one notices his hands, which are unusually large and hirsute, and clumsily modelled. They are hands in which all other qualities appear to have been sacrificed to that of strength: yet they are capable, in fact, like his nature, of surprising delicacy. He moves through life, rather ponderously, in an aura of pipe-tobacco and antiseptics.

During the seventeen years in which he has practised at Monk's Norton, Dr. Hemming has become (apart from Miss Abberley, whose supremacy is a matter of faith rather than of reason) by far the most important person in the village. He is its friend, its counsellor, its universal confidant. He is admitted to share the troubles that shadow men's minds as well as the most intimate ills that affect their bodies. He is their comrade, rock-firm, in the major emergencies of birth and of death, and a source of rich humanity as well as of practical wisdom.

He is not a brilliant man professionally; his prime medical asset is his knowledge of his own limitations, and the fact that the most skilful of his colleagues in North Bromwich know him, like him, and are ready to help him. He is neither cultured nor erudite; he does not pretend to understand or appreciate any beauty but that of Nature. You have only to enter his house—the black-and-white seventeenth-century building with the brass plate next to the post-office—to realize these deficiencies. The furniture is comfortable common-place Tottenham Court Road, with a sprinkling of black oak that has little to commend it but its age. There is no piano. There are no pictures and no books to speak of: it is doubtful if Dr. Hemming has bought, since he came to Monk's Norton, a single volume that is not concerned with medical science. By his bedside table, beneath the accursed night-bell, you will find, indeed, a small bookcase containing the library he acquired in his student days. There are cheap reprints of Bacon, Montaigne and Darwin, Macaulay's Essays, Green's *Short History of the English People*, Boswell's *Johnson*, Gibbon's *Decline and Fall*, and a number of Hardy's novels on India paper. These are relics of a secret past. His present contains no secrets save other people's.

In his house, as in his life, there is no shelter for secrets—not for even so much as a spider's web, a piece of fluff or a dropped pin; and that is no small achievement in a building so warped and so full of shadows. It owes this almost surgical order and cleanliness not to Dr. Hemming, who, however efficient he may be professionally, is not by nature a tidy man, but to his wife.

Mrs. Hemming has all the virtues. When her husband first met her, in his "resident" days at the Prince's Hospital, she was Sister-in-charge of Number Two Theatre; and the habit of discipline acquired in controlling that white shrine of glittering sterility, where each instrument had its place, where the very floors and walls were aseptic and the loss of a swab or the momentary misplacement of a scalpel or pair of forceps might spell disaster, has persisted in her married life. She is a little, neat, silent woman (in the theatre one does not talk much), with serenely watchful eyes and a sweet but determined mouth. She has no more intellectual interests than her husband, but can do anything with her hands, which are small and wiry, like the rest of her, and always inclined to be red, as though they had never quite recovered from their former perpetual scrubbings in hot antiseptic solutions. No emergency—and there are plenty of sudden alarms in a country practice—perturbs her in the least. Whatever happens, she can be trusted to keep her head and to hold her tongue. Though she is not popular in the way that her husband is—Dr. Hemming's bluff, obvious honesty makes him all the world's friend—she is universally respected, and by nobody more than by him.

He is prepared to admit that she is "more than half of the show." She keeps his visiting-list and his day-book; she "enters up" accounts in the ledger and makes out the bills; she sterilizes his instruments and dispenses prescriptions and sees that everything is in order in the midwifery-bag; she holds the fort when he is away on his rounds—can give "first aid" to cuts and sprains and fractures and, at least, prevent people making fools of themselves. She is, moreover, though she knows everybody's business, the soul of discretion. It is partly because of this, perhaps, that she has made no intimate friends: partly also because, as a doctor's wife, she is anxious not to be suspected of "running after" people for professional reasons, and again because, although she is proud of being one, the social position of a doctor's wife in a small community is slightly equivocal. She cannot, she knows, however polite they may be to her, pretend to mix on equal terms with "the county"; on the other hand (and this is a pity) she feels she cannot quite afford to be intimate with Miss Martin or even with Miss Burlingham, the district-nurse with whom she has so much in common. As a result of these social inhibitions it would be natural if Mrs. Hemming felt herself somewhat isolated. She does not. There are few busier and there is no happier woman in Monk's Norton than she. For two-thirds of her life she has been brought up in a world that considers doctors the most important as well as the noblest members of society, and she regards her husband, whom she mothers and adores, as the best of the species. Their one child, a boy, born soon after they came to Monk's Norton, is at school at Epsom, and will become a doctor too, as a matter of course.

The surgery, approached by side-doors in the passage leading to the garage at the back, shows the influence of Mrs. Hemming's passion for order and cleanliness as much as the rest of the house. It is a converted coach-house divided into three small compartments: a public waiting-room opening into the doctor's consulting-room, and, separated from this by a wooden screen backed with shelves, the dispensary whose sharp odours of medicinal tinctures and antiseptics permeate the air of all three.

Dr. Hemming's waiting-room—particularly on a Friday morning when his panel-patients bring their club-cards to be signed—presents a cross-section of Monk's Norton society as representative as Fred Perry's bar on a Saturday night or the church on Sunday. It is also revealing because it indicates in brief the kind of minor ills Monk's Norton flesh is heir to. There is always a certain number of old people who find their way to the surgery for no other real reason than that they are old; that the human machine is beginning to show signs of hard wear and rough treatment, and is gradually breaking down. Many of the men are farm-labourers who suffer from backs and joints distorted and sinews stiffened with rheumatism—partly as the result of prolonged and inevitable exposure to foul weather and the wearing of rain-sodden clothes, partly, too, because they have spent the remainder of their lives in the damp and darkness of the picturesque hovels "down the road," in which they have little chance of "shaking off" these infirmities or the chronic bronchitis which makes them breathe hardly and racks them with "winter-cough." "I shall get the better of it all right," they say, "when the apples are in blow."

Their wives visit the surgery more rarely. Their relatively sheltered life protects them from the continued soakings and freezings that foster rheumatism, and, in any case, few of them are insured against sickness. When they "go to the doctor's" it is generally to lend the encouragement of their company and experience to some shy younger woman, or perhaps to confess to some malady that has been wearing them down until they can bear it no longer: often enough the legacy of forgotten child-birth—a neglected prolapse that has become inoperable cancer, or a patch of eczema, gradually wearing through to produce that nightmare of working-class womanhood a varicose ulcer, which the myriad advertisements of quacks selling ointments call "a bad leg."

One spectre haunts the back of all these old people's minds: the Workhouse Infirmary. Though the local authorities build palaces to house them and give these new names, the ancient stigma remains. They would rather crawl painfully up and down stairs from their beds to the fireplace, or die of neglect and cold and starvation under their own rotting thatch, than be skilfully tended and warmed and well-fed in "The Union." Dr. Hemming knows this. Among other things he is Medical Officer for the Parish; it is often his job to strike a delicate balance between suffering and pride, between bodily ill and mental distress, and the tact with which he achieves this is one of the reasons why he is loved. It is more important, he holds, to understand than to treat. And persons come before cases.

Old age, of itself, is the commonest ailment in Monk's Norton. That is why there are not many young or middle-aged people on the waiting-room's varnished benches. The fact that they come to the surgery at all, instead of sending for Dr. Hemming to visit them, implies that their troubles are not very grave. It is by no means a grim assembly. One can hear a good deal of gossip and chatter and even laughter that is hushed and falls to a sudden silence as the bell on the doctor's desk rings or his gruff voice calls "Next, please." There is usually a woman or a child with a swollen face tied up in a handkerchief, which signifies a gumboil ready for lancing or a tooth to come out. The teeth of Monk's Norton people nowadays are not what they should be, and will not be much better, the doctor tells them, until they stop eating soft food, and devitalized stuff out of tins, and the pappy white bread on which Bagley, the baker, prides himself. There is always a sprinkling of the common casualties of labour: poisoned fingers infected by the prick of a thorn or a splinter; small bones broken or chipped in wrists or ankles by a fall, and greenstick fractures in children; cuts and grazes and bruises that have to be stitched or dressed. There are a number of convalescents: some who long to get back to their work and others who dread it—but the latter are rarer, because work means money and money means food, and even when there is sick-pay to be drawn it is not easy to feed a grown man, let alone a young family, on the savings put by from an agricultural wage of thirty shillings a week.

So the bell on the doctor's desk rings and the waiting-room slowly empties, until finally nobody answers the call of "Next, please," and now the main work of the doctor's day begins. Mrs. Hemming has his list ready. New calls and urgent cases usually come first; but the order in which they are set out is mainly dictated by the lie of the land and the run of the road in such a way as to save him covering the same ground twice; and in the maze of twisting lanes that surrounds Monk's Norton this planning is no easy matter. By eleven o'clock, as a rule, the garage is empty and the old car racketing away on the morning round, while Mrs. Hemming, having restored the surgery to the order which is the pride of her methodical soul, hurries back to the house and sees to the preparation of the doctor's dinner. If the round is a short one and easily planned, he may be home by one-thirty; but more often the meal has to wait till two and be spoiled, and then unceremoniously bolted: in a doctor's house there can be no such thing as a regular mealtime. And, when it is finished, as likely as not, a batch of new messages may have come in, which will compel him, wastefully, to cover the same ground all over again; but before he sets out the morning's prescriptions must be entered up in the day-book and a dozen bottles of medicine dispensed and labelled, and set in an orderly row on the waiting-room shelf to be called for that afternoon.

It is the area he has to cover and the fact that he works single-handed rather than the number of his patients that makes Dr. Hemming's life so full and his task so exacting. In a season when sickness is prevalent it is rare for him to get an afternoon to himself. He may snatch an hour or so between tea and the evening "surgery," which opens at six; and even then, when the waiting-room door has been locked and the lights turned out, and he settles down to supper and a quiet perusal of the *Lancet* or *British Medical Journal* and the *North Bromwich Courier*, which are his only reading, while his wife "makes up" the books for the day, his time is not really his own; even later, when, drugged with the fresh air which is his calling's main physical compensation, he has knocked out his last pipe and yawned and gone up to bed and

straightway fallen asleep, there is always the chance of the night-bell or telephone ringing. Mrs. Hemming always wakes first. A habit that has survived from her early years of training in hospital makes her sleep lightly with senses keyed-up to confront an emergency. Before he has stirred she has taken the telephone-receiver or slid up the window to see who is standing below. Her sharp, businesslike voice confirms the form of the message, and calmly passes it on to him:

"It's Jim Pipard. He says his wife was 'took bad' two hours ago. It's all right, the nurse says, but she thinks you'd better come. He sounds scared to death. What shall I say?"

"Mrs. Pipard? Oh, yes, I remember. What a damned nuisance! Why couldn't she wait till daylight? Tell him not to worry. It's her first, but she's perfectly all right. Just say that

I'll come. If he likes to wait I'll take him along in the car with me."

Dr. Hemming dresses by candlelight and goes stamping downstairs. Mrs. Hemming, in spite of his protests, follows him and hands him his black leather bag. As she returns to her cold bed, she can hear the roar of the starting engine and a grating of gears (Dr. Hemming is not a good driver) and the whine of the worn transmission as it dies away in the distance.

Dr. Hemming sits in the car, encouraging the tremulous young husband: he knows what it feels like, he says, when your wife has her first. He is now wide awake and aware, once again, of the strange exhilaration that comes to a man when, roused from slumber, he finds himself suddenly transported and whirled into the emptiness and silence of the nocturnal earth. He has often before seen Monk's Norton and the woods and the great rolling claylands transfigured by sleep; yet each time that he sees them—in spring when the headlights' beam reveals plum-blossom flecking bare orchards like flurried snow, in midsummer nights when the sky never loses all light, when hedgerows are pallid with billowing clouds of elder-bloom and gauzy ghost-moths eddy in the beam like wind-blown petals; in autumn, when mist lies in vagrant patches, like fog at sea, and earth is trackless as sky; on November nights when stars glitter like powdered crystal, and meteors, unseen by other men's eyes, slide silently over the vault and flare and are gone—in all these rare manifestations of beauty he is made aware of the earth's solemn magnitude and of a mystery in which his own insignificance and that of all the transient human life which he tends are the strangest part.

These ecstatic, unreasoned, sudden perceptions of awe and of beauty are, perhaps, Dr. Hemming's nearest approaches to a mystical or a religious mood. He is not, in the ordinary acceptance of the term (the Rector's, for example), a religious man. He is too nearly concerned with the defects and the weaknesses of men's mortal bodies and with the obvious emergencies of existence, such as birth and death, to trouble himself much about their immortal souls. Yet not even the most captious or cynical of his neighbours can deny that, according to his lights (which are those of broad day: these nocturnal exaltations being, in his case, a lapse from the normal), he is a good man: the better perhaps because, in spite of the pitiful degradations of human flesh and spirit with which, on occasion, his practice confronts him, he has a natural inclination to see good in his fellow men. If he is not particularly gifted or skilful—and he doesn't pretend to be either—he is kind and honest and wise and courageous and merciful. Whatever the next world may hold in store for him, he has his reward in this: it would be difficult in Monk's Norton (or all England) to find a more happy man.

"DOWN THE LANE"

V

"Down the Lane"

IF, returning from "down the road" past the doctor's surgery and skirting the Sheldon Arms you turn sharp right, leaving the green and the stricken oak on your left, you will always be said, in Monk's Norton, to have gone "Down the Lane." Why "down" it is hard to say; for the Lane runs as nearly dead level as the adjoining cricket-pitch, and only shelves downward a foot or two at the point where it dips into the watersplash. Perhaps your descent is social rather than physical, marking the difference of level between such prominent institutions as the Church, the Manor, the Rectory, the Surgery and the Pub (in that order of precedence) and the less important buildings that border the Lane. They are, naturally, not so dignified as those at the Cross; for the Lane, though it was once a salt-way trodden by pack-horses and quite possibly, also, by the legions of Ostorius Scapula, has only become part of the village's cruciform anatomy during the last hundred years—during a period, that is, in which the sense of style in architecture has unfortunately been lost.

Though it shows a certain amount of thatch there is no black and white and very little half-timber, while Monk's Norton's latest and proudest possession, the Village Hall, is a lamentable essay in concrete roofed with galvanized iron. Such attractions as the Lane does possess—and it is not without charm—depend on the mellow tones of the tawny brick of which most of its cottages are built, and on the beauty of the gardens in front of them. It would seem that all the best gardeners in Monk's Norton live down the Lane, unless it be that the soil in that part of the village is kinder, or the land's greater relative elevation prevents frost lying. Their gardens, in any case, are redolent with the perfume of old-fashioned blooms, such as wallflowers in Spring and stocks and sweet-williams and phloxes in Summer, while their rustic arches and pergolas and the porches protecting the cottage doors are smothered in a luxuriant growth of roses and honeysuckle and purple clematis.

One sees at a glance that these people love their gardens and are proud of them. It is obvious, too, that there is a strong spirit of competition among the gardeners. Whenever a new showy plant, from which seeds or cuttings or shoots or offsets can be taken, appears in the "big house" gardens, it is only a matter of time before it mysteriously crops up in "the Lane": in isolated cases at first, but later as a fierce epidemic. This happened, unluckily, some years since with the Wichuriana rose called

Dorothy Perkins, which, at one time, bade fair to smother all that part of the village with its odourless papery trusses at the expense of older, more richly-scented blooms. It has happened also, more fortunately, with the Penzance briars, which have found their way by degrees into every hedge, and drench the Lane at night with hot wafts of their vagrant perfume. On the whole it seems that colour and opulent growth appeal to these cottage-gardeners more than scent; and perhaps, though the sense which colour excites is less subtle, they are right; for in the seasons of fullest bloom the whole air of Monk's Norton is so saturated with natural sweetness of mown-hay and meadow sweet and wild mints and hedge-roses that the addition of exotic scents may well seem superfluous.

But before one reaches these cottage-gardens, other odours must be noticed. All the more memorable country smells of Monk's Norton are associated with the Lane. First of all comes the bakery, kept by Mr. Bagley, which smells every day, when his wood-fired ovens are opened, of hot new bread, and on Sundays in Summer, when thrifty folk grudge fuel, of baked meats and potatoes, whose appetizing fumes escape from the roasting-tins in which children carry them home to middle-day dinner. There are not many loaves left on the shelves an hour after baking is over; for Mr. Bagley's son drives most of them out on his round in a hooded pony-cart. Yet even when no scent of hot crust remains, the baker's shop is permeated by the nutty odour of flour that lies finely sifted everywhere—not only on counter and floor but on Mr. Bagley (and Mrs. Bagley) themselves, giving their features and hair a look of dry pallor, and so dusting their clothes that they resemble in their working hours bees covered in pollen or mealy cock-chafers.

On the opposite side of the road to the bakery yawns the black throat of Joe Ferris's smithy. Like poor Mr. Webber's, his business has felt the pinch of mechanical competition from Mason's garage. In the first days of motoring, when Miss Abberley's Daimler was a novelty, Joe Ferris, as the only person acquainted with metals, was often called on to straighten a bent axle with crowbars or beat out a buckled wing. Now spare-parts are so cheap and so easily obtained that nobody dreams of taking a car to the smithy, nor even a tractor. The repairs that come to his anvil are mostly those he was brought up to deal with: snapped tow-chains and traces and broken harrows and plough-coulters blunted or twisted by tree-stumps or stones. There is still, thanks be, a certain amount of shoeing to be done, and horses must still be "roughed" in Winter when the roads turn to ice. In that country of irregular fields and abrupt dips and hillocks the tractor is still looked upon as awkward and dangerous, and horses start up more easily than motors on a frosty morning. So often enough, on the cindery patch in front of the blacksmith's shop, you may see a patient team of huge horses waiting to be shod, and watch the pulsating glow of the hearth and see the sparks fly, and hear the leathern wheeze of bellows, the tinkle of hammer on anvil and its thud on red iron, and—far more provocative than all those sights and sounds—smell the ammoniacal reek of singeing horn, which is the most memorable, because the most potent smell of country childhoods.

There is a wheelwright's shop, Mr. Beazeley's, next door to the smithy, and that, too, has its proper odour, subtly different from that of the carpenter's shop, though its sources are mainly the same. Mr. Beazeley uses three woods to fashion wheels for his waggons: wych-elm for the nave, heart of oak for the spokes, and ash for the felly (he never calls it a "felloe": no more did Hamlet)—three English woods with Anglo-Saxon names—and every one of them growing green in the fields round Monk's Norton! It is a sweet, clean, native craft, this wedding of wood to wood, and a brave sight too is one of Mr. Beazeley's huge wains (he still builds one occasionally, although such work wears for ever) in its barbaric colouring of blue and vermilion, a vehicle that seems almost too mighty for one small, wizened man to have made with his hands. How he finds space to house and erect such monsters it is difficult to imagine, his yard is cluttered with such a variety of vehicular debris: detached axles and springs and broken-down dog-carts and waggonettes and jingles and milk-floats, that stand piled against one another like farmers' traps at a sale.

At the back of the shop, in a shed to themselves, are two specimens of the coach-builder's art of which he is particularly proud. They are the carriages the Miss Abberleys sold, nearly thirty years ago, when they "took up" motoring. One is a "Brougham," on "C" springs, built in the eighteen-forties; the other a "Victoria," not quite so old as Miss Abberley herself. The first is upholstered in striped tabaret, the second in morocco and moth-eaten melton; and the furniture of both, door-handles and road-lamps, is made, Mr. Beazeley maintains, of genuine silver.

"They may talk about motor-cars," Mr. Beazeley says, "but just look at the curve of this panelling! Quarter-inch 'Onduras Me'ogany, that's what it is, joints primed with white lead, though you couldn't guess there was one. Twenty coats of copal varnish, sir, neither more nor less, on the top of it. That's coachbuilding, that is! It does your eyes good to gaze on it! And them there spokes: just look at the lightness and strength of them! That's none of your American 'ickory; that's heart of oak. I know, for the 'ickory shrunk, and my grandfather made new ones. You'll never see wheels to touch them there on the road to-day, nor anything like it."

You will see very few carriage-wheels, nor will Mr. Beazeley make them. As the farmers buy trailers and motor-cars, their discarded traps accumulate as junk in his cluttered yard which backs on the schoolroom, a building of decent red brick, slate-roofed, and the playground in which Miss Martin's flock perform physical exercises. At the end of their morning's work, when these young yahoos pour out shouting and screaming into the Lane like a stampede of wild ponies, you might imagine them completely unmannered and undisciplined. As a matter of fact that shrewd and stalwart young woman has them well in hand. When you pass by during school hours, you can hear them bleating like lambs. Mrs. Sheldon-Smith has been heard lamenting that the little girls no longer curtsey to her and that the boys do not raise their caps—a shocking state of affairs which she attributes to Miss Martin's politics; but the fact remains that, under Miss Martin's tuition, more and more of these children pass on from the village to the secondary school, and that their lives, when she has done with them, are full of a number of civilized interests outside the elementary curriculum: they have learnt something about simple poetry and folk-song and animals and birds and flowers, and have been taught that there is more in life than making a living; and Mrs. Sheldon-Smith, regretting the vanished curtseys, forgets that when first Mr. Jagger cycled into Monk's Norton, small boys threw stones at him.

Just beyond the schoolroom, standing back a little from the road, is the small, trim cottage occupied by Miss Burlingham, the

District Nurse. Sometimes you may see her bicycle propped against the garden gate; but not often, for she is not only the most hard-worked but also (with Dr. Hemming and Miss Martin) the most efficient and valuable person in all Monk's Norton. The gods have not overburdened Miss Burlingham with graces. She is a thick-set, bustling, bunchy middle-aged woman with a ruddy wind-scorched complexion and wispy red hair. It is difficult to examine either her form or her features in repose, for the spectacle she usually presents is one of perpetual motion, a fugitive vision flashing past on a bicycle.

Miss Abberley, in conspiracy with the doctor, is mainly responsible for the nurse's presence and persistence in Monk's Norton. Before she was imported and established (and that was only at the end of the war) there was no such thing as skilled nursing available in the district. Wounds were dressed with lard spread on linen and poulticed with lettuce-leaves or bathed in cold tea; aged folk, too feeble to tend themselves lay helpless and patient until their bony backs wore through to bedsores; women in labour were left to the dangerous attentions of an ancient witch whose proud qualification for the practice of midwifery was the fact that she had had more children than anyone else and had buried seven of them and who, crawling louse-like from house to house, complacently carried her dirt and her septic infections from one patient to another. In Mrs. Higgins's day no woman remained in bed for more than a week after childbirth, and during that time Mrs. Higgins (whose function was, in theory, to do all the housework as well as looking after mother and child) strained the family resources by living on the fat of the land, including a "spot of something" in her tea. As a consequence, the rate of maternal and infantile mortality was, for a normally healthy rustic community, terrific. Mrs. Higgins was more than satisfied if her unlucky patients "reared" three babies out of five.

Nurse Burlingham has changed all that. Though there is no money to set up a pre-natal clinic in Monk's Norton, and a busy housewife must think twice before she can get a day off or face the expense of a visit to Worcester, the lack is made good by Miss Burlingham's amazing energy and mobility. To and fro, like an anxious hen, she scurries, covering all her wide district on her elusive bicycle, carrying the buoyant cheerfulness of her weathered face, the reassurance of her presence, and, above all, her shrewd tolerance and inexhaustible common sense, wherever she goes. Neither degradation nor dirt can daunt this apostle of sanitation. From her spotless uniform, with its snowy starched collar and cuffs, and her face, which always looks as if it had recently been scrubbed with carbolic soap, there radiates a veritable aura of passionate cleanliness which envelops all places and persons with whom she comes in contact. She is utterly tireless; her working day has no settled end or beginning; at the close of it she will cycle five miles and spend a whole hour doing the work of a charwoman in the cottage of some lonely and grubby old man. She has an eye like a hawk for children with snuffling noses and running ears: no septic tonsils or faulty teeth escape it. Her persuasions have even exorcised from the minds of Monk's Norton people their ingrained dread of hospitals. If she had leisure (and, of course, she has none) it is doubtful if she would know how to use it. She has no pronounced personal tastes (or taste) and no secret desires, save the hope that, some day, she may be able to afford a small second-hand motor-car—not because this would save her sturdy legs, but because it might help her to cram into the short span of twenty-four hours a day a dozen more "cases." In one sense she is a lonely woman; she has no social standing and no friend. In another she need feel less lonely than anyone else in Monk's Norton; for everyone welcomes her, and the whole village is her friend.

Nothing has ever been known to flurry Miss Burlingham or find her lacking in decision. On the occasion, for instance, when Captain Grafton, going home in the dark, mistook her house for his own and then, having found the front door locked and no key in his pocket, climbed in through the scullery window and groped his way skilfully upstairs to her virginal chamber, Miss Burlingham did not, as a weaker woman might have done, exhibit alarm. She just asked "Who's there;" and snapped on her electric torch; then said quietly, "Oh, it's *you*, Captain Grafton, is it? If you'll just wait outside on the landing I'll be with you in a minute. But for goodness' sake keep away from the stairs till I come!" Then she guided her visitor downstairs and out of the house and led him to his own door and found the missing key in his trench-coat pocket and made him sit down while she took off his boots and put him to bed—just as if incidents of that kind were part of her everyday work.

It was, Captain Grafton maintained, the sort of thing that might have happened to anybody on such a foul night. His cottage and Miss Burlingham's stand side by side, and are almost indistinguishable from one another in shape and size. The only difference—and one which he might have noticed—is that his has a name. It is the only house of that modest type in Monk's Norton (except Ivy Cottage) that aspires to this quite unnecessary dignity. Any letter addressed: Capt. A. P. Grafton, would certainly find him; there is only one Archibald Grafton in the village and no room for another; but Captain Grafton (as "dear old Mahrie Lloyd" used to sing in the "Grand Old Days") believes in the beneficial effect of indulging one's fancies; and, since he "fancied" *Etaples* (which Monk's Norton calls "Eatables") as the name for his cottage, he painted it boldly in white letters on his green garden-gate.

Captain Grafton, like Mr. Jagger, is, geologically speaking, an intrusive—or as Shelton, the thatcher, who likes using long words, declares, an "anteloper": the confusion in Shelton's speech-centre, may possibly have arisen from the heads of horned game which infest the cottage walls. In Monk's Norton he is usually known as "the Captain" or, behind his back, as "Archie." He arrived in the village soon after the war, without any excuse except that he had been shell-shocked and gassed, and accordingly needed quiet for the nerves and fresh air for the lungs. His only territorial association with this part of the world was his having once, as a gunner-officer, been brigaded with the Worcesters and having found them "damned stout fellows."

It is "the Captain's" chief tragedy (though he does not know it), that he survived the war, which was not only the climax of his existence but, probably, the only part of it that nature qualified him to justify. He is a case, Dr. Hemming would charitably say, of arrested development: though whether any development that matters was lost by the arrest, is a question more debatable. After all, Captain Grafton's type is one that must have been recognized in the aftermath of every great war in history. Shakespeare knew his peers and drew them incomparably, and Monk's Norton, with the accumulated wisdom and tolerance of ages, has had no difficulty in accepting him for what he is, if not for what he imagines himself to be.

He is a spare man, just short of fifty—though he feels (and thinks) like a boy—with thin hair plastered down by some kind of fixative that conceals its greyness and a toothbrush moustache clipped short with the same object. His complexion is raw and of a permanent redness due not to the natural glow of health but to a network of fine arterioles congested, perhaps, by the effects of poison-gas and, certainly, by alcohol. He has pale blue eyes which, when you examine them closely, are not bold, as they seem at first, but pitifully frightened. His voice is resonant, though generally rather husky. He likes to use it in church and in hailing folk from a distance as though he were shouting orders on a barrack square, and similar suggestions of his military career survive in his costume. He usually wears khaki shirts, with a zig-zag gunner's tie, and cord riding-breeches, covered in Winter by a greasy trench-coat or a British Warm. The remnant of the service tradition shows itself too in his limited vocabulary, still embellished with wartime slang and allusions to things forgotten which nobody younger than Fred Perry can understand, and in his attitude towards politics and life in general, which is that of a puzzled schoolboy, nursing a grievance against the changed values of these degenerate days, yet constrained, out of soldierly pride, not to make a fuss. It is difficult, of course, to see the way in which everything for which he and his friends fought and suffered is going to rack and ruin without active protest. But the old guard can still pack up its troubles and do its bit. Captain Grafton does it, with a solemn sense of duty, at meetings and armistice-day parades of the British Legion (when he puts on his medals) and also as Scoutmaster. Beneath all these activities, one suspects, what he most desires is to enforce and submit to discipline (which wouldn't be bad for him) and to wear a uniform. The Scoutmaster's shorts and slouch-hat are only a childish substitute. He feels more important and happier and more "like himself" on the rare occasions when he dons a black shirt and a belt and sets off with a loaded cane in his hand to parade with the North Bromwich Fascists. Then, at least, he feels that England has need of him.

In spite of these little absurdities "the Captain" is a popular figure in Monk's Norton. He is known as a "sport." He has a smile and a joke for everybody. When hounds meet at the Cross he is always there, cleared for action, with a bulldog pipe in his teeth and a green felt hat, with a jay's feather in it, set jauntily aslant on his head. At "smokers" or village concerts he can tune his barrack square voice to a sentimental song and recite Kipling's *If* with unaffected emotion. When the Village Hall has to be cleared for dances or entertainments or political meetings, he is there in his khaki shirt-sleeves to set up the platform and, if speakers on his own side get heckled, to act as a chucker-out.

The boys and young men of the village adore him, because, although he is undoubtedly a "gentleman," he is no snob. In the cricket-field he is a reckless and usually unsuccessful hitter. Though he takes the game seriously, as part of the English tradition, he never (like Major Sheldon-Smith) appears to resent getting out or to mind being slightly ridiculous. The older men like him too. He can pass without the least awkwardness from the captious cronies of Mrs. Perry's sanctum to the labourers in the public bar, and is good for a round of drinks in either of them at times when his pension has just been paid and he has money to spend. And the wives of Monk's Norton also have come to approve of him; for they know that although he makes risky jokes which occasionally shock them there is really "no harm" in the Captain; he has never presumed on the advantages of his bachelor station by "interfering" with village girls. They think it is a pity that such a nice man has never married, and him so fond of children, not knowing that one essential part of his traditional code is the distinction between "ladies" and "women." He could never dream of marrying anyone but a lady, and no man of honour in his circumstances could possibly expect a lady to share them. As for "women" . . . they, of course, are another matter. There are plenty of women in North Bromwich where he goes, every month or so, to spend a mysterious week-end "with friends!" Who his friends are, nobody—not even his best friend Mr. Rudge—can say. For gentlemen never tell.

A pathetic, if not quite an admirable figure—poor Archie Grafton with his attempts to maintain the old military smartness, his perpetual anxiety to do the soldierly thing and live up to the code of the ante-room. In spite of his forced activity and affectation of manly zest his life must be pitifully empty. That, no doubt, is why he habitually fuddles himself and finds refuge from time to time in the sort of "binge" that brought him, blind to the world, to Miss Burlingham's bedroom. His life virtually came to an end in nineteen-eighteen, and nothing less than another war can resuscitate him—by which time (if the dreadful thing come) he will be too far gone to be of very much use. Like everybody else who served actively in the war, he is a wounded man, and a sick man, too: the high colour that flames in his cheeks is a sinister symptom. A man is as old as his arteries, and his arteries are not too good. One of these days, Dr. Hemming has warned him, if he takes too many liberties, the walls of some tiny blood vessel in his not very brilliant brain will probably give way—and then: good-bye to the Captain! There is no harm in him, and much good-nature. He is, as kind people say, no man's enemy but his own; and he has no real friend in the world but his neighbour, Mr. Rudge.

Mr. Rudge lives next and last down the Lane, in a regrettable bungalow of which he is excessively proud, opposite the patch of allotments in which the village's surplus horticultural energy finds vent. It would be hard to discover a couple of neighbours and friends more dissimilar than Captain Grafton and he. Mr. Rudge cannot, like his neighbour, be described as an anteloper. The Rudges have staked their claim to belong to Monk's Norton in a good many square feet of the graveyard's surface. At the time of the Civil War (or the Rebellion, as Miss Abberley calls it), they owned the Goodrest Farm. Now all that remains of their landed property is the small-holding of fifteen acres which Mr. Rudge inherited ten years ago from a second cousin.

Before this, like Mr. Jagger, he had been vaguely "in business"; but the inheritance, which was unexpected, must have awakened in his mind some atavistic desire handed down to him in the "genes" of his yeomen ancestors; for no sooner had he "come into" the property, which consisted of more or less equal parts of poor pasture and neglected orchard, than he threw up his business, realized all his meagre possessions, and decided, at the age of forty, to settle in Monk's Norton and live the simple life. For this venture Mr. Rudge brought with him an elderly housekeeper, a lamentably inadequate capital sum, and no qualifications except a naïve and boundless enthusiasm and a mystical conviction that all his troubles were over.

On the contrary, they were only beginning. By the time he had built his bungalow and sunk a well, more than half his small capital had vanished, and the land, on whose produce he proposed to live, had barely been scratched. Mr. Rudge was neither discouraged nor deterred. When his spirits wavered, he had only to look around him and tell himself proudly that this plot of solid earth was veritably his own. He was a landed proprietor; and it was a heartening thing, as he told Captain Grafton—who, having unlimited time on his hands, was delighted to receive his new neighbour's confidences—to be one's own master and to know that the fruits of one's labour would not go automatically into someone else's pockets.

Having spent all his previous life in the handling of figures, Mr. Rudge had a pathetic confidence in their infallibility. It was demonstrable on paper, as he explained, that each acre of land should produce a definite sum every year—roughly, say ten pounds as a minimum. One able-bodied man could certainly deal single-handed with fifteen acres; and on three pounds a week, together with surplus produce, a man who had no extravagant tastes should not merely be able to live in comfort but to put by money.

Captain Grafton, who had no head for figures himself, was profoundly impressed by these calculations; he gave it as his considered opinion at the "Sheldon Arms" that this fellow Rudge had his head screwed on all right; he was even tempted, in moments of dissatisfaction with his present aimless life, to compound his pension and set up, under Mr. Rudge's guidance, as a small-holder himself. But this was not all. Mr. Rudge also showed conclusively that the reason why many small-holders failed to make good lay not only in their ignorance of first financial principles but also in their silly habit of putting all their eggs in one basket and hoping for the best. It was inevitable, he maintained, that one should sometimes lose on the swings: it was equally reasonable to count on making up on the roundabouts. "If you have a bit of everything," he maintained, "you can't go wrong. Every successful business man recognizes the necessity of 'spreading his risks.'" Nothing, Captain Grafton agreed, could be clearer than that.

Mr. Rudge spread risks lavishly over all his fifteen acres: another of his principles was that one should not spoil the ship for a ha'p'orth of tar. By the time he had finished stocking it with Wessex Saddleback pigs, Kerry Hill sheep, short-horn cows, runner ducks and Rhode Island Red poultry, and replanted half of the orchard-land with Victoria plums and Cox's apples, he had made another big hole in his dwindling capital. Yet this did not distress him. The proceeds were there to be seen: to be seen far more clearly, indeed, than money locked up in a bank or in other people's industries. He was not even perturbed when the first years of farming showed no profit. Once established, his theory of an economic circle was unassailable. The land, to start with, was his own; the pigs and the poultry would fertilize the land which, in return for this generous treatment, would grow pasture abnormally rich to feed the cows, and the cows' surplus milk, in its turn, would feed the pigs' litters, and the money that rolled in from the lambs and the piglets (at least twelve to a litter) would pay for the food-stuffs that nourished the Saddleback sows and the poultry. Conservative estimates, taken from the best authorities, conclusively proved that, when once the cycle was set in motion, the swarms of livestock could go on, in theory, supporting each other indefinitely—as indeed, up to a certain point, they undoubtedly did—while the produce of the orchard would provide an increasing income.

In practice, unfortunately, they failed to support Mr. Rudge and his housekeeper in addition to themselves. There were, he was forced to confess at last, certain elements in the business which did not conform to the rules of compound arithmetic, certain flaws in the theoretical foundations of this House that Jack built. He had not counted, for instance, on the fact that, quite apart from losses by foxes, his stock of poultry would not live for ever and that, in any case, after three years their laying capacity would diminish. He did not foresee, when he cut his first crop of mistletoe from his cousin's aged apple trees, that his ewes would nibble the fallen sprigs in the orchard and be poisoned and slip their lambs. He did not know, when he bought the old sheds second-hand for his pigs, that the wood was infected with mange, or that rabbits bred tapeworms and puddly ditches liver-fluke. He did not realize that when snow falls in Winter, not even the most persistent sheep can find enough feed to keep it, and that these self-supporting animals must then be fed on hay. It had never struck him that the prices of food-stuffs varied within such widely terrifying limits, nor that a weaner or lamb which sold for twenty-five shillings in Worcester market one week might fetch less than twenty the next; nor had anyone warned him (since it was none of their business) that the well he had sunk at enormous and unexpected expense for his bungalow was inadequate to quench such a multitude of thirsty throats, and that, even if well-water were good for animals (which it wasn't) it would have to be pumped and carried before they could drink it. And, beyond all these things, no figures had made him aware of the fact that there does not exist any slavery on this earth so grinding and so interminable as that which is imposed by animals on the human beings who have to look after them.

Three years of single-handed mixed-farming revealed poor Mr. Rudge as a haggard, exhausted and disillusioned man, marooned among hordes of hungry or sickly animals. Disillusioned, but not disheartened. He was a resolute creature. One Tuesday, returning from one of his North Bromwich week-ends, Captain Grafton, "popping in," as he usually did, "to see how things were going"—his faith in the tightness with which his friend's head was screwed on remained still unshaken—was bewildered by an unusual silence and staggered to find that not a single head of livestock, apart from the poultry, was visible on the holding.

"I sold them on Saturday," Mr. Rudge told him, cheerfully, "every damned one of them. If you'll run your eye over these books you can see for yourself. These figures prove conclusively that a mixed holding is uneconomic. It's all down there to the last farthing: you can't get beyond figures, my boy. If I hadn't been able to check it by accurate costing, I might have gone on indefinitely losing three pounds a week. As it is, I'm just on thirty shillings in pocket since I saw you last—and that, mind you, without lifting a finger, apart from feeding the fowls!"

"I hope this doesn't mean we're going to lose you, old boy?" Captain Grafton asked anxiously. "You're not giving up?"

"Giving up? My dear fellow, what on earth are you talking about? I'm only beginning. During the week-end I worked out the figures. If you'll run your eye over this paper. . . ."

And Mr. Rudge went on to explain his new economic theory. Why were stock-prices low and food-prices high? Because frozen meat came in every day by the shipload and glutted the market; because we grow so little corn ourselves that we have to import it. (Captain Grafton looked puzzled; he felt there was something wrong there; but his mind was so dazed and impressed by the figures before him that he could only nod approvingly.) Very well, then, the obvious solution of all the small-holder's difficulties was to produce only such things as the foreigner couldn't: a genuinely fresh egg, tender salads and perishable soft fruits.

"I shall re-plant all that's left of the old orchard and break up the rest of the land gradually for plums," Mr. Rudge declared. "Those new Coxes I planted are just coming into bearing, so I shall let them stand for a year or two. The blossom looks kind. Barring frosts, we shall pick a good crop. Coxes always sell well."

"You just send for me when you want 'em picked, old boy," said Captain Grafton, "and I'll pick the lot. You gave me a bit of a shock, you know, when I came here this evening. But I'm sure you're right. You'll be making a mint of money before you've finished."

There was no frost that year late enough to pinch the apples, and yet, in the whole of the orchard, not a single fruit set. Mr. Rudge and his friend surveyed the bare trees with perplexity.

One evening that Summer he came hammering at the Captain's door. He was flushed with excitement.

"I've got them," he cried. "I've got them at last!"

"Got what?" said the Captain.

"Bees, old fellow. Six buzzing hives of them. It came to me like a flash in the middle of the night. All those blessed apples wanted was bees to fertilize them. And now I've got them! What do you think of that?"

"Old boy, I congratulate you," the Captain said earnestly. "I should never have thought of it."

"I've worked it all out, if you care to look through these figures," Mr. Rudge continued. "It's not merely that you can count on a full crop of apples: there's the honey as well. Now a good hive of bees gives you forty pounds of honey, and good honey sells at one and sixpence a pound. That's sixty shillings a hive, and six hives means the best part of twenty pounds sterling a year—eight and sixpence a week. When I get into the run of it I shall probably take up bees on a larger scale."

"I'm not going to help you keep bees, old boy," said the Captain firmly. "In Africa, when bees turn savage they're the very devil. I knew a fellow who damn near got stung to death."

"English bees don't sting much," Mr. Rudge said confidently. "And if they do, I'm told it's good for rheumatism."

All that Winter Mr. Rudge fed his bees with cane-sugar; all next Spring he ecstatically watched them pollinating his apple-orchard. Once again the blossom was kind; once again not a single fruit set. It was only a casual remark in the bar of the Sheldon Arms that put Captain Grafton on the scent of the source of his friend's misfortunes. Cox's Orange Pippins, it seemed, were not self-fertilizing. What they needed for fruiting was cross-pollenization by some different kind of apple such as a Worcester Pearmain. He hurried away to the house of his friend to break the bad news tactfully.

"Those wretched Coxes?" Mr. Rudge said. "Oh, don't worry about *them*, old fellow. I've been spending the last three days in grubbing them out. And I'm scrapping the bees as well by the way: they've got Isle of Wight disease. Now *plums*. . . ."

Mr. Rudge continues to live—or at least to exist—on his plums. It is, he admits, a somewhat chancy business. When there are plenty of them they sell for as little as one-and-sixpence a pot of seventy-two pounds: when they sell for twenty-four shillings a pot they are usually so scarce that it makes little difference. If you grow early varieties, they have to compete with imports from France and Italy. If you grow late ones, they come in at a time when everybody has eaten so many plums that they are sick of the sight of them. If there is a glut, the canners and bottlers are in a position to beat you down. If they are scarce they are in a position to do exactly the same, having canned or bottled all they need in the last year of plenty. These are not idle statements. Mr. Rudge can prove them by figures, and is always ready to do so on the least provocation.

He is still, in spite of his numerous ambitious failures—which include, in addition to these, disastrous adventures in jam-making rhubarb-forcing and mushroom-growing—an incurable optimist.

He no longer has the air of adventurous prosperity he wore when he first came to Monk's Norton. His clothes are threadbare; his neck has the skinny look of a plucked chicken; his whole body looks somehow shrunken except his little pot-belly, which is spanned by a silver watch-chain. He is rather hard of hearing —even the Captain has to shout when he "pops in" for a smoke of an evening—and his eyes are not quite what they were. Yet, from first to last, his hope and enthusiasm have never wavered. Though he has given up trying to make a fortune for himself on the land, he can still demonstrate mathematically exactly how it can be done. And whether you make a fortune or not, he will tell you, no life can compare with that of the small-holder.

"FARMER'S GLORY"

VI

"Farmer's Glory"

Mr. RUDGE could have saved himself a great deal of trouble, to say nothing of money, if he had condescended to seek and follow the advice of George Collins of the Goodrest, his nearest neighbour on the farther side of the Brandon Brook. Though the brook, which defines the Western march of his property, completely separates George Collins's farm from Monk's Norton, he not only "belongs" to the village but also, in many ways, is its most important inhabitant. He certainly pays bigger rates and gives more employment than any other. He is Rector's Churchwarden and Vice-chairman of the Parish Council and of the school Managers. He represents Monk's Norton on the County Council at Worcester, where he sits on the Highways and Bridges Committee and has done a great deal for the betterment of the local roads.

In spite of this influential position, he has never (as folks took it for granted he would) persuaded the authorities to erect a bridge over the Brandon Brook at the end of the lane. This is partly, no doubt, because of his strict sense of responsibility in the handling of public money. It is also, perhaps, a symptom of the intense sentimental conservatism which is part of his nature, and of an anxiety not to "spoil" a picturesque feature in his private landscape which he has known from a child. So the watersplash, with its cressy shallows, its beds of alien monkey-musk and spires of loosestrife, remains as a barrier between his farm and the village. On week-days his muddy motor-car charges through it—for he is a furious driver, being always in a hurry, and knows all its soundings by heart. On Sundays, he and his family walk to church in single file over the rickety footbridge which has always seemed on the point of collapsing, yet never collapses.

The watersplash, indeed, is the only right approach to the Goodrest, and a proper prelude to its particular delights. The lane, on the farther side, immediately assumes a neglected air: lush verges impinge on it and grass grows on the crown between the winding wheel-tracks. Only the hedges on either side of the track, which degenerates—or at least becomes wilder—as it climbs a ridge of low hills between bluebell-sheeted coppices to Eastward, betray the fact that they are under the strict control of an orderly mind, having been laid and pleached and determinedly trimmed as often as they showed the least sign of getting out of hand. Twenty yards from the ford, on the right hand side of the road, a white gate, which, like all Mr. Collins's gates, hangs well and swings easily, admits one to the field called Long Dragon Piece (or Long Dragon for short), through which runs the road that leads to the farm, and whose reptilian shape conforms to the willow-bordered curves of the brook.

In cuckoo-time there is no sweeter plot of land near Monk's Norton than Long Dragon Piece. It is just so far from the village that none but the faintest evidences of its existence—the anvil-tinkle from Ferris's smithy, the starling-babble of children let out of school, or the clear quavering note of the tenor-bell slowly tolled for some old man's funeral—can reach it. It is so near (but for the brook) that one is always consolingly aware of human neighbourhood. The Long Dragon has never, in living memory, been "put up" for hay, and Mr. Collins is the last man in the world to depart from that kind of tradition. As a consequence, though lightly grazed, it is as rich in flowers as an Alpine lawn. The banks of the brook and the willow-boles are starred with primroses. In the moist hollows that drain it grow lush beds of king-cups with glossy, kidney-shaped leaves and sappy stems, and Horse-mint and Hairy-mint and tiny-flowered Forget-me-nots, invaded by silvery drifts of Lady's Smock, the cuckoo's own flower, which hang like a motionless mist of lilac close to the ground. But the greatest glory of Long Dragon in early May lies neither in king-cup nor lady's smock, but in the scattered myriads of cowslips whose downy peduncles, shot up (as it seems) in a night from the grass whose growth lags behind theirs, cover all the rising slope with a pale dust or bloom, resembling in hue the wings of a brimstone butterfly, and drench the air with faintly vinous perfume.

It is the pallid freshness of these blossoms—primrose, cowslip, lady's smock, and catkins of hazel and sallow—with its suggestion of being tender and fragile and newly-born like the lambs which pasture among them, that gives Long Dragon in Spring its air of faint unreality and enchantment, of elation and sadness. The scene is limned with so rare a line and washed with such limpid delicacy of colour (many boughs and twigs are still bare, and no masses of full-grown leaf overburden the shadows) that it seems not merely a manifestation of supernal loveliness, but a symbol of beauty's transience and an urgent admonition to partake of that beauty before it vanishes, while the warm wind carries the breath of the cowslip-bells, and the lady's smocks shiver in silver, and the lazy lambs that dapple the field seem soft as the clouds that sail high above them, and the very note of the cuckoo, endlessly calling, seems mellowed and hushed by the depths of air in which it is floating.

There are many lambs in Long Dragon Piece at this season. Mr. Collins believes in latish yeaning, when the keep gets more growth in it. He crosses the Kerry Hill ewe with the Suffolk ram, and their offspring combine the nimbleness of their dams with the sire's sturdy build, his black stockings and his smooth sleek head of dusky chestnut. Mr. Collins's ewes show no maggot-eaten patches of their fleeces, nor limping foot-rot either; for he has his own dip, and the whole flock goes through it three times a year and walks from one field to the next through a foot-bath of blue vitriol. The lambs lie on the vivid green as white as new-born mushrooms; they lie close to the road, so sleepy with food and drugged with soft air that one must almost tread on them before they trouble to scamper away to their mothers.

For a while the road runs roughly parallel with the Brandon Brook. Half-way through Long Dragon it swerves uphill to a ridge from which, on one side, the roofs of the village are seen, and on the other the farmhouse and noble barns of the Goodrest. When (or if) Charles II slept there, he cannot have seen the irregularities which now give the farm so much of its charming character. It was built in the year he was born, and at the time of Worcester Fight had barely attained its majority. It is a large H-shaped two-storeyed building of brick and half-timber, with tiled roofs and twin attic-gables, both dominated by a projecting ashlar-based chimney with triple diagonal shafts. Its original windows, which were probably oak-mullioned, have gone, and the mean wooden framing that has replaced them detracts from the house's dignity. Inside, successive owners have made havoc of the ground-plan; but the heavy adze-marked ceiling-beams remain, together with an oak staircase with moulded strings and handrail and banisters with Ionic capitals, and in all the down-stairs rooms there are remains of period panelling, square or linenfold, adapted impartially to the walls for the sake of warmth and comfort rather than for beauty, and generally smothered by heaven knows how many coatings of paint.

If it has lost a good deal of stylistic grace, the Goodrest is still a solid and comfortable house befitting the solidly comfortable family who dwell in it. The furniture is mostly modern and makes no pretensions to elegance; nor is there any display apart from the considerable collection of plated cups and tea-trays and servers and coffee-sets which Mr. Collins has won at cattle-shows and in the competitions arranged by sellers of seeds and fertilizers for the best-grown crops or the best-kept farm to be found among their customers. And the Collins's manner of life is in keeping with their surroundings. Prosperity has never tempted them to "launch out" or "make a splash." Though they have never grudged themselves anything in reason—good, plain food in abundance and winter warmth and such minor luxuries as a first-rate wireless set and comfortable arm-chairs—there is no sign of extravagance. The two sons and the married daughter have been given the advantage of an education superior to that of their parents. The girl went to a Malvern boarding-school, and the boys, after leaving Bromsberrow, were sent to Schools of Agriculture: one to Wye and the other to Cirencester. Mr. Collins continues to pride himself on being an old-fashioned farmer; he makes a show of laughing at his sons' scientific modernity; but though he pretends to distrust theoretical learning, he is shrewd enough to listen to all they have to say and, having pondered it, to give their ideas a trial.

"You chaps," he says, "are always in such a darned hurry."

Mr. Collins is never—or never appears to be—in a hurry. He is a big, lumbering man, with a humorous mouth, shrewd, twinkling eyes, and enormous blunt-fingered hands. For a man of his weight and figure he is surprisingly active, and, apart from an occasional twinge of lumbago, does not know what it is to be sick. On the farm, whose eight hundred acres he manages to cover without fail every day—even when public business or markets take him to Worcester—he generally appears to be lost in slow contemplation. You will find him, as likely as not, leaning over a gate and watching his crops and his livestock—particularly the "Grade A" shorthorn herd and large white pigs, which he rears on the Danish system.

"I like pigs, you know," he will say: "they eat so hearty; and I like to see the way their hams rub together."

But suddenly, as he is gazing, the shrewd eye will harden:

"Excuse me," he says—he is always polite—and shouts to the stockman. "Jim, what's up with that gilt's near hind-leg? I don't like the way she's moving. If there's any thickening, give it a rub, and starve her to-night and drench her with salts in the morning. And ask Mr. Bert to have a look at her anyway. Understand?" Then he smiles; his tone changes: "My boy Bert, you know, he fancies himself as a vet. These lads who have been to college, they think they know everything. And they *do* know a good bit, mind you, though it's better not to let them know that you think so." Mr. Collins chuckles apologetically. As a matter of fact he is intensely proud of his sons.

As, indeed, he should be. Between them, governed and guided by their father's wisdom, they have made a good deal of difference to the earnings of the Goodrest Farm. A large part of the higher land has always been known as poor pasturage. The boys are changing all that. By persistent pitch-poling and harrowing and limeing and slagging, and cows fed and milked on the Hosier system and poultry following in folds, they are gradually replacing the sour *agrostis* pasture by wild white clover and ryegrass. The gorse and insurgent bracken which once invaded the upper fields has been kept in check. Looking down from the crest of the hills one can almost distinguish the extent of the Goodrest lands from the surrounding property by their astonishing greenness. By gradual stages the farm is being mechanized. When Mr. Collins bought his first Fordson—there are three tractors now—the village grew anxious. This abominable invention, it was whispered, would put men out of work. On the contrary, the Goodrest, to-day, employs far more men than ever before and gives better wages. Only himself and the Inspector of Taxes knows the extent of Mr. Collins's income. It is probable that he pays more in taxes, as well as in labour, than anyone else in Monk's Norton: and a great part of this is return for the money he spent on his sons' education.

"Yes, they're good boys," he says. "I've no complaints to make —except that their mother spoils them."

Mrs. Collins spoils all her family—and nobody more than her husband. She, too, comes of an old farming stock and understands farming ways. She is three or four years older than her husband, but hardly looks it, for her face is unwrinkled and has the ruddiness of a Worcester Pearmain. Observing that face, one might guess that life has treated this woman kindly. And so, on the whole, it has. Her unmarried life, over to Westward in the Teme Valley, was calm and sheltered. Marrying rather late —she was twenty-seven—she found, in George Collins, a husband whose upbringing and standard of life and social milieu were precisely the same as her own, so that moving from Temeford to the Goodrest implied no great dislocation. Nor did she come there empty-handed. Her possessions, though modest, were sufficient to assure the respect which is one of the principal advantages of a marriage of convenience. If the couple were not passionately in love they had material interests in common; and the successful furtherance of those interests in which both had a stake has given their marriage unshakeable stability. Mrs. Collins has never had reason to complain, like poor Mrs. Hawley, of her husband's unfaithfulness. Even if George had been "that sort of man" (which he certainly wasn't) he would have had to think twice before he indulged in such inclinations, for this placid woman is much the stronger of the two, and he would have paid for them heavily. People say she has been "the making of him," and, up to a point, this is true; for the man's easy-going nature needed the precise kind of stimulus which hers supplies. But luck had a say in the making as well. They were lucky, for instance, in the fact that their sons were too young to go to the war and that Collins himself, though of military age, was considered by the recruiting authorities an indispensable man engaged in a "key" industry. They were lucky, again, to have been able to embark on the expansions in which her small fortune was sunk at a time when land was cheap and the prices of farm-produce were rising; they are lucky, too—though here, once more, Mrs. Collins's influence counts—in having begotten two sons in whom their separate virtues, his shrewd solidity and her energy and strength of character, have combined to produce the best type of modern farmer.

Now the crucial point of their endeavours is over. The family, prosperously settled on its lands, should be safe for the next hundred years. But Mrs. Collins is not the woman to rest on her oars. Though most of the milk is sold to North Bromwich by contract, she still keeps a small dairy and will be up at five on a Summer morning for butter-making. The Goodrest butter has made a name for itself, and she has her own contracts made for it with the best grocers in Worcester. She handles the poultry, too, selling brown Rhode Island eggs and scrupulously dressed Light Sussex fowls and Aylesbury ducks. The money that comes to her from this trade (and it must bring in a steady income) is her perquisite. Her husband chaffs her about these mysterious savings; but if either of the boys needs any modest luxury—such as a dress-suit or a new motor-bicycle—Mrs. Collins can always find money to pay for it in her secret hoard. In addition to running the dairy, she controls the house (they keep only one servant), pots eggs, bottles fruit, makes jams and chutneys and ketchups, pickles walnuts and onions, cures bacon and hams, and does the best part of the family cooking as well. Though she never seems flustered or moves in a hurry, she probably puts in more hours of work in a day and walks more miles than her husband.

When she has a moment to spare, you will usually find her "poking about" in the garden. It is not in the least a "gardener's garden" (like Mrs. Sheldon-Smith's) nor a formal pleasance (like Miss Abberley's); it is not like these two—nor even like the cottagers' gardens that beautify The Lane—an expression of living human personalities. It is, rather, if such an idea be reasonable, an expression of the personality and the accumulated experience of the Goodrest itself: somewhat overgrown and neglected (since no labour is wasted here on anything not economic), with moss-grown box-edged paths, straggling bushes and cankered fruit-trees which, if anyone had any time to spare, should have been grubbed out long ago. Its flowers are all old-fashioned and mostly sweet-scented: grey bushes of lavender and rosemary (which only flourish, her husband says teasingly, where the woman rules); moss-roses and silvery-pink *La France*, and clove-carnations and balm and self-sown sweet-williams and evening primroses. It is a tangled wilderness which, one might think, would offend such an orderly mind as Mrs. Collins's; and yet—perhaps for the very reason that it is so different from the rest of her surroundings—she loves it dearly; never loves it more, indeed, than in Spring when the snowdrops have gone and velvety polyanthus and double-daffodils are in flower, and the old jargonelle pear-trees which, rising on either side of the ashlar-based triple-stacked chimney, are flattened, like monstrous ivy on the flank of the house and clothe its ancient shape with stiff trusses of dazzling white, so that, by day, its glory resembles that of a bride, and by night, beneath mere starshine, still glimmers like a tall ghost.

How old those old pear-trees are, none can say for certain. Mr. Collins boasts that he reckons they are as old as the house itself, and few people in Monk's Norton care to dispute Mr. Collins's judgment. In any case, the cool Goodrest marl is kind to deep-rooting trees. All over the land that slopes to the brook there are scattered occasional pyramids of the native Wild-pear (or Choke-pear, as some would call it), whose fruit, when it turns from green to gold and falls in November, is collected in sacks and carted to the mill to make perry. Monk's Norton, Mr. Collins maintains, is no cider country, though he usually makes half a dozen hogsheads as well. His own drink, like his father's before him, is Worcestershire perry, which must not be broached till next year's blossom appears. The stuff, as he makes it—pure pear-juice unfortified by raisins or barley-sugar, and racked into new sherry-casks—is an elixir of clear, pale amber, dry and slightly rough to the tongue, with a faint ferruginous aftertaste like that of a Förster Jesuitengarten or one of the choicer Auslese Liebfraumilchs. Mr. Collins is reasonably proud of this beverage, and says there is no drink like it. When he also declares that there isn't a kick in it, you may treat what he says with more caution, though it is certainly less vicious than his port, which his wife buys at three and sixpence a bottle from the grocer in Worcester.

On the opposite side of the Lane from Long Dragon, a field called Jericho, of much the same shape and of hardly less enchantment, follows the left bank of the Brandon Brook. Its farther hedge is the Northern limit of the Goodrest land, as a close observer might guess by the character of its husbandry; for the field next beyond it—even taking into account the fact that the soil is possibly poorer—grows so rank with squitch and other species of couch-grass and is so beset with creeping plume-thistles and burdocks and stag-quicks of bird-sown hawthorn, that Mr. Collins's lazy white lambs could not crop a living off it. It belongs to the d'Abitot estate, and is leased, along with some seventy acres attached to the Mill-house in which he lives, to a farmer called Hallow.

One calls Mr. Hallow a farmer by courtesy or by charity. Mr. Collins and his sons would say he is nothing of the sort. Their standards are certainly high; yet they would not speak so indignantly if they had not suffered from his neighbourhood. Mr. Hallow's unruly hedges are full of glats through which cattle (not unnaturally) stray on to the rich Goodrest pasture. Mr. Hallow's silvery thistle-beds, disputed in Autumn by greedy packs of goldfinches, launch flights of floating seed over the Goodrest fallows. Mr. Hallow's impoverished ploughland breeds pestilential charlock whose offspring finds a happier home in the Goodrest's careful tilth. Mr. Hallow himself is a difficult, jealous, ungenerous neighbour, always ready to make complaints and to borrow machinery which he is in no hurry to return.

This is not altogether poor Mr. Hallow's fault. It was not his good fortune to marry a wife with money. He was not, though older than Mr. Collins, permitted to stay at home during the war and make hay under that baleful sunshine. During those years, his farm, which has never been much to boast of, was left to the mercy of an elderly and slovenly foreman who let everything deteriorate. The Mill has never recovered from that period of neglect, and probably never will until the day, perpetually imminent yet never arriving, when the d'Abitot trustees get tired of waiting for their arrears of rent and put in an execution and turn Mr. Hallow out; when the Collinses, with their mechanized thistle-cutters and slag-drills and all their paraphernalia of progress and modern efficiency, swoop down on the hostile fields and restore them to order and cleanliness.

Yet, in spite of the obvious material defects of its present condition, Monk's Norton mill, when it comes into the Collins's hands (as it is sure to do, sooner or later) will lose much of its character. There is a field-path right-of-way wandering down from the middle of Love Lane, at the back of the church, which crosses the Brandon Brook by the top of the dam at the foot of the mill-pond and follows its course all the way to Jericho. This path provides a favourite Sunday afternoon stroll for Monk's Norton people. Though their character differs from that of Long Dragon, the fields in which Mr. Hallow's nondescript cattle are grazing have the charm of the wild. His broken hedges are turbulent with wild roses and crab-apple, and the coarse, tufted slopes that fall here more steeply to the brook are as thickly set with primroses as Long Dragon is spread with cowslips. The banks are so steep that flood-water has made naked patches of tawny soil whose poverty can only nourish the resistent flowers of arid upland pastures such as milkwort and lousewort

and agrimony and harebells and scarlet pimpernel; but amid these meagre blossoms there settle and flutter perpetually the small, restless denizens of dry places: common blues, with the dove-grey speckled underwings, and small copper butterflies.

The brook, too, in this part of its course falls more rapidly, and can even be heard, with a tinkle of mountain-water flowing from stickle to pool; and the pools themselves, shadowed by boles of unpollarded willows that lean over the stream and meet overhead like the vault of a tunnel, have a dark, secret look. In the swirls at the sallows' bases big trout have their holts. They are the only game fish to be found in the Brandon Brook. Captain Grafton, always the sportsman, has proved their existence by hauling one or two out on a "white moth" dapped under the branches at night; but Mrs. Perry, compelled to eat them out of politeness, confesses, in private, that they taste as muddy as roach. In the midst of the tunnel there is always a kingfisher's nest, and the burning blue of the startled bird can sometimes be seen as he flashes upstream and threads the dark channel with his electric streak.

From the bottom of the little gorge through which the stream runs to the level of the sluices that feed it, is a steepish pitch, and the path, with its steps of slippery clay, makes no easy climbing. It is only when you reach the top of the dam that the pool it contains and the Mill-house beyond become visible. Mr. Jagger, our prime authority in such matters, considers the Mill the most interesting building, excepting the church, in Monk's Norton. This is partly, no doubt, because his researches in the register have revealed the fact that his putative ancestor, Ambrose Jagger, lived and died in it; but, apart from this personal bias, there is much to be said for his claim. For one thing, the Mill is mentioned in Domesday: "*At Nortona Monachorum, Abbot Walter of*

Evesham holds ten hides and one virgate, a mill of the value thirty pence a year and a vivary (or stewpond)." Mr. Jagger asserts that Norman work is still to be seen in the massive sandstone foundations on which the visible remains of a fifteenth-century half-timbered house and its successors are based.

Of itself, apart from the obvious picturesqueness of the channelled race and the stationary wooden mill-wheel whose bucket-troughs perpetual drippings keep green with moss and slimy waterweed, and of the lanterned dovecote with steep-pitched gables that stands nearby, the Millhouse would not seem in any way a remarkable building. There is no grace of proportion in its shape; the windows are too few and too small; the whole place wears the slovenly air that might be expected from Mr. Hallow's depressing tenancy. It is only when to this uninspiring picture there is added, beneath the green strip of bank, an inverted image of the grouped buildings of gabled dovecote and house together—submerged and refreshed (as it were) in the still, translucent depths of the mill-pond—that one becomes aware of another element in the picture: a pervasive sense of unreality—as though this quite ordinary house were not what it seems but had been subtilized by some mysterious variety of enchantment which reduces the tangible brick and its watery image to an indeterminate state that makes it hard to tell which is substance and which reflection. In the pride of noon, when the sun beats down on the water, discovering in its depth suspended motes of vegetable matter and shadowy shoals of perch, flashing back from the flat leaves of the water-lilies which grow thick wherever silt has made the pool shallow, and from the brittle wings of halcyon-bodied dragonflies, the house and its image appear to withdraw themselves from that play of fierce light. Their magic shrinks and wilts in it; they await their moment. That moment comes when the last breath of moving air has ceased to trouble the water and the last direct ray of light has faded out of the sky. Then, as though utter stillness were necessary for the manifestation of a spectral beauty that brooks not the faintest commotion, the shapes of the gabled buildings and of their inverted ghost detach themselves from the background in which they have been withheld; and fill the eye. There is no life in the side of the building that rises sheer from the millpond; its windows are cobwebbed and sightless, no light enlivens them: the house on the bank and the house under the water are one in their rapt and deathlike trance. Strangely solemn they seem, and even a little sinister in their immobility, commanding silence, commanding stillness as a condition of their continued existence—until, perhaps, a watervole plops or a rising fish dimples the surface, and the spreading wave rocks the image in its matrix of fluid ebony, or a white owl, noiselessly circling the dovecote, rips the tissue of silence with its rippling cry; and then the millhouse is no longer a lovely phantom, but the scene of poor Mr. Hallow's material embarrassments: a damp, tumbledown building, infested by rats, for which rent must somehow be paid.

He does manage to pay his rent sooner or later, or else it is certain he would not remain at the Mill; for the d'Abitot trustees are an impersonal body, without any bowels of compassion for a defaulter. They leave him alone because they know he has grievances on his side as well. There is no denying that the structure, for which they are responsible, has been neglected, and that parts of it are falling to ruin; that the roofs of the out-buildings let in rain; that there isn't a single practicable gate on the farm, and that no new tenant would take possession without involving them in a large capital expenditure; and the d'Abitot trustees, heaven knows, have no capital to spare.

Meanwhile Mr. Hallow drags on his meagre, haphazard existence, contriving, by some miracle of providence, just to make both ends meet. He is a lean, quiet man, with dejected, drooping moustaches and gentle honest eyes which have always a puzzled look. What puzzles them more than anything else, except the constant problem of finding money for the rent, is the growth of restrictions and regulations that have complicated the pursuit of his calling in recent years. All these dratted Milk Boards and Pig Boards and Marketing Schemes, he believes, are inventions of the devil deliberately devised to plague him. The mere sight of a buff envelope or of Constable Homes is sufficient to terrify him, for he feels that whatever he does by the light of nature and custom is likely to be wrong and to stamp him as an offender in official eyes. The lost paradise of his past, on which his mind dwells wistfully, is the time when he worked for his father before the war, when a farmer could do as he liked and the Ministry minded its own business. His present is spent in living from day to day and from hand to mouth; and his future will not bear thinking of, for he has no sons to follow him.

Since everyone in Monk's Norton likes the man and most are sorry for him—there are many jealous old stagers, indeed, who prefer his inertness to Mr. Collins's triumphant energy—it is usual in the village to put down Mr. Hallow's troubles to his wife, a "stranger" whom he "picked up" at the end of the war in a London suburb, when he was wounded in hospital and therefore "not accountable."

Mrs. Hallow is certainly a shrewish, slatternly townswoman, who understands nothing of country ways and is not a good "manager"; but there is more to be said in extenuation of her discontent than Monk's Norton will allow. At the time when her husband married her, she was a good deal younger than he, a pert, gay, quick-witted and not unattractive girl, accustomed to the brightness and bustle of suburban streets, fond of dance-halls and lighted shop-fronts and cinemas. No doubt the idea of marrying a farmer, a solid man who was his own master, seemed to her a step up in the world, and the prospect of having a fine big house of her own in the country romantically idyllic. But the country itself, as well as the country people, with whom she had nothing in common, declined to accept her easily; and the big house of her own, with its lack of all urban conveniences, proved itself a burden rather than a satisfaction. As its mistress she found herself working for longer hours and harder than a domestic servant, and with less reward for her labour. Its isolation bored her, its silence got on her nerves. She hated its mud and its unremitting drudgery. She would have been better off, she told herself, if she had married a man who worked for a modest wage, but brought it home regularly on Saturday to a house in a row with water laid on from the main, and indoor sanitation, and a gas-stove put in on the hire system. She was lost, she found, in a backwater remote from the stream of life as she knew it, and as stagnant as the mill-pond itself, condemned by her marriage-lines to live there for the rest of her life. And she has no children. In her heart she is even jealous of the cowman's daughter, Bessie, who has had a bye-child in Bromsberrow Union. Is it any wonder, after all, that she "lets things go"?

Mr. Hallow has far too many anxieties of his own to worry about her complaints. His days are as long and as exacting as hers. When they are finished, he flops down on the bed and sleeps like an animal. When he drives her to market she finds herself, as often as not, marooned in the waiting trap, unnoticed and lonely, while he wets his bargains with dealers and butchers in the bar of the "Hop-pole." He has no interests outside his farming, and no conversation. There are weeks on end when he hardly speaks a word to her. When he has an odd moment to spare of an evening, his first instinct is to escape from her shrill voice and bitter tongue. Then he takes out a gun and shoots rabbits—the banks and hedgerows are riddled with burrows—or fits up his worming-rod and fishes for perch in the pool. He will stay on the bank above the sluices for hours, his melancholy eyes fixed on the float; and this irritating abstraction (though she does not know it) is his sovereign solace. He sits there, forgetting the Pig Board, the Milk Board, the d'Abitot trustees, and even his wife, in rapt contemplation of the still pool's glassy surface, of the house that rises above it and the other house underneath—the house in which he was born and hopes he may die—and of the twilight landscape of which, oddly enough, his motionless, shabby figure seems an essential part.

And, of course, Mr. Hallow must go. There is no reprieve for him. His end is inevitable in an island society that imports two-thirds of its food. His going is to be regretted as little as that of the water-mill, which, sooner or later, the Collins boys will replace by a turbine. He is kindly and pitiable; well-meaning and inefficient; a good man, as men go, but a bad citizen. Let this be his epitaph.

THE VILLAGE AT PLAY

VII

The Village at Play

THE life of Monk's Norton, generally, is not nearly so full of material anxieties or so lonely as poor Mr. Hallow's. It is—as Captain Grafton, who believes in squeezing the last drop of juice from the orange, maintains—a "sporting little place: by which I mean, old boy, that a fellow with no spare money to chuck about can enjoy a bit of everything in the way of sport cheap and keep his liver in trim." By the time the cuckoos come the fox-hunting season is nearly over; but the last meet is usually held on the green in front of the "Sheldon Arms." When there were two Miss Abberleys, hounds used to meet at the Manor House; but the strain of being gracious to so many people at once has, of late, been rather too much for the surviving old lady; so, rather than risk the social blunder of transferring the meet to The Grange, the Hunt has compromised by holding it just outside her garden wall.

On the morning of the meet the village is early astir. All its normal activities are suspended; the shops are deserted; before the hound-van arrives from the kennels a small crowd of foot-followers, of every age and condition, has assembled under the shadow of the stricken oak. The captain is there early, of course. He wears a full-skirted riding-coat of a large check pattern; an Ascot stock-tie held in place by a pin with a fox's head on it; cord riding-breeches, whose buttoned "extensions" bulge beneath his stockings; dull, dubbined shooting-boots with their tops encased in canvas anklets, and a rakish green Homburg hat with a jay's feather in the band. He conceives it as part of his duty, as a sort of liaison officer between those who are sportsmen by birth and the aspiring but ignorant masses, to instruct novices how to conduct themselves in the hunting field: to teach them how to behave at the cover-sides, when they should holloa, and when they should not; and to insist on the unpardonable enormity of heading a fox and of calling a hound a dog or its stern a tail. It is his duty also to collect, on behalf of the village, all scraps of local information likely to be useful—such as where foxes have lately been seen, or have ravaged poultry. He does this in a loud, commanding voice, which grows even louder when the Miss Sheldon-Smiths (or one of them, with their father) ride up. Mr. Sheldon-Smith gives the captain an off-hand salute; but the Miss Sheldon-Smiths, though they know quite well who he is, prefer to look down their noses or in the other direction, because they consider it a flagrant social solecism for a man who has merely fought in the war to retain the military title a grateful Sovereign has given him: a right which, they strongly feel, should be reserved for regular soldiers, many of whom have never yet seen a shot fired in anger. Though it is quite safe to bow or even to say a few words on the subject of the weather to such people as Mr. Collins, or Harry Hawley, or even Fred Perry, people who "know their place," a bounder of the captain's type is much better kept at a distance.

Not that Captain Grafton cares (or allows them to see that he cares) whether they bow to him or not. The complaisant ladies of his North Bromwich adventures are nowadays much more in his line than these stuck-up dummies! There is no nonsense of that kind about real ladies, he says; and he knows what they are, old boy, because he was nursed by more than one of them in the war; and if the Miss Sheldon-Smiths imagine they can put their pitiful snobbishness over on *him*, they are greatly mistaken! In any case he is far too busy and important at the moment to bother about them. He would much rather talk to real people, such as Walter, the huntsman, who grins and touches his velvet cap to him, and the whippers-in who stand warily watching the hounds as they roll on the grass; to say nothing of genuine aristocrats such as the master (a gunner like himself), and Colonel Ombersley from Chaddesbourne, and young Lord Wolverbury—all of whom are ready to give him a cheery "good-morning" and call him "Grafton," without any "Captain" or "Mister," as if he were one of themselves.

And now, as the clock in the tower strikes eleven, the group clustered at the Cross is increased by the whole body of Miss Martin's schoolchildren, who, released on the stroke of the hour, have come tearing like a stampede of wild ponies down the length of the lane. Captain Grafton has his eye on them, and the boys have their eyes on him too, for they have been taught that a meet is a serious occasion on which they are expected to behave like scouts and Englishmen. As they crowd to the green the captain keeps them back with his loaded cane, forbidding them to encourage the hounds, who would like to play with them, reducing them to an awed and gaping silence, while the master, in friendly consultation with Mr. Collins, decides which cover to draw first—till, at last, the word goes round: "Pritchett's Wood . . . Pritchett's Wood . . ." The old men nod approvingly: "Ay, they'll find one in there for certain"; and the captain, always useful, shouts: "Get out of the way there, you boys!" while the meek pack trots through the alley he clears and the horsemen walk after them with a clopping of hoofs; and a crowd of motors, crawling in bottom-gear, brush the eager press of foot-followers with their wings, and the whole excited concourse goes streaming away down the lane, past the bakehouse, the smithy, the Village Hall and the school, to the watersplash, and the grass-grown road that climbs from Long Dragon—till, at last, the subdued babel of speech and the clatter of hobnails and horseshoes die away on the soft spring air, and the Cross, deserted, is left to its wonted silence.

Often, during that day, Monk's Norton will hear sudden crashes of distant music, or the melancholy quaver of a horn drifting down from the bluebell woods on the ridge above the Goodrest. These are the sounds of a winter morning. More typical of the village at play are those that one hears down the lane on a warm evening in May when the roped square in the middle of the cricket-field has been mowed and rolled, and the clean crack of leather on bat-willow echoes through the air. Though the lads of Monk's Norton play football in autumn and winter, cricket is the village's darling pastime. There is hardly a cottage in which you could find a man, young or old, who has not attempted to play the game, and who does not still cherish a passionate interest in it. The "wireless," which penetrates nine-tenths of them, keeps that interest green. If, in Winter, on Saturdays, they listen for the results of League Football, it is because most of them, as Mrs. Bentley, the post-mistress knows, have small stakes in the "penny-pools"; but in Summer, on every evening of the week, they listen for cricket scores because their interest in county cricket is an integral part of their natural lives. It is symptomatic, no doubt, of our native frivolity that when ministries fall or embattled powers disagree, or whole continents are ravaged by flood or drought or shaken by earthquakes, Monk's Norton barely troubles to think what these catastrophes mean; but when Worcestershire, on a crumbling wicket at

Kidderminster, beat Yorkshire by eleven runs, the whole village is instantly abuzz with triumphant delight; and while a great poet or statesman may lie on his deathbed without exciting the slightest concern, the state of Harold Larwood's toe or Bob Wyatt's jaw is a matter of acute anxiety. The intimacy of this benevolence is shown by the way in which favourite players are always spoken of by their Christian names. The young men of Monk's Norton work too hard during the week, and play too hard on Saturdays, for most of them ever to have seen their heroes perform in the flesh, nor has one of them the remotest chance or hope of playing for Worcestershire; yet Reg. Perks and "Doc." Gibbons, Cyril Walters and Dick Howorth and, more lately, "the Honourable Charles," are names as familiar in their mouths as if they were their own boon-companions.

This is a charming foible, and native to these red marls. It is, moreover, characteristic of the spirit of a game which has more good fellowship in it than any other. There is no sweeter sight in all the Monk's Norton summer than that of the cricket-field encircled by a thin line of critical onlookers intently watching each ball and every stroke, or clustered about the little pavilion and score-board; that green sward scattered with the shapes of the fielders—some in flannels which seem, at a distance, incredibly white, others clad in their working clothes with their shirt-sleeves rolled up—all unconscious of everything but the zest of the game. And the sounds associated with this scene are pleasant too: the click of the bat and the thudding of a fieldsman's boots as he races to save a boundary; the players' good-humoured chaff; the spreading ripples of easy laughter or loud applause in a game which can be as comic as it is serious; Captain Grafton's barrack-square voice bawling out: "Well hit, well hit!" or appealing: "How's that, sir?", the umpire's laconic: "Not out"—

and, above all these, in the summer sky, whose soft hue, faintly veiled, is like that of a holly-blue butterfly's wing, the notes of invisible cuckoos and of the church clock striking the hour that seem to hang on the air or float in it as though its warm density sustained them.

On the benches in front of the pavilion, older men, who have played in their time, discuss and dispute over matches that they remember, with one wary eye on the game. Neither village —nor county cricket, for that matter—is what it was in their days: there are no batsmen now like Jessop or Archie Maclaren or the Foster Brothers, no bowlers like Lohmann or Richardson or Wilfrid Rhodes. In twenty years' time the old men on the benches will be speaking with just as much pride of the players their fathers belittled. There is every reason to suppose that the game will go on in Monk's Norton as long as the church tower stands. It is a symbol, for one thing, of rural democracy: on the village cricket-field, as in the graveyard, all men are equal—apart from the captain of the side, who is just as likely to be the local blacksmith as the squire. For another, though the Monk's Norton side are as anxious to win their matches as any northern county, they are not greatly distressed when (as usually happens) they lose. For cricket to them (as Stevenson said of walking) is mainly a matter of "certain jolly humours," a diversion in which the essence of all summer joys is distilled. When they cannot play neighbouring villages they are content to play amongst themselves. They begin their game as soon as their work is over, and only draw stumps when the light is too faint for the ball to be seen.

The young men are more fortunate in their pastimes than their wives and sisters; yet the leisure of village women, if there be such a thing, is far richer to-day than ever before. To begin with, there is hardly a cottage in all Monk's Norton whose chimney is not disfigured by a wireless aerial. Through the distortions of their cheap "sets" and loud-speakers there filters continually a flood of much that is noble, if more that is base: the symphonies of Brahms and Beethoven alternating with the deliquescent whinings of "crooners" and the primitive sophistications of "hot jazz." Not that the sublimities of music affect them much more than its perversions: for most of them both are just Sound—a friendly and quite unimportant accompaniment to their workaday activities, and an antidote to loneliness. With the wireless switched on, whether they listen to it or no, they have a comfortable feeling that they are not alone in their isolation: it is the voice of the great world magically invading their closed existence and making them vaguely yet thrillingly aware of its own. How much of the beauty (or even of the ugliness) that is impartially thrown on the air succeeds in penetrating and influencing their subconscious minds, it is hard to say; but the spoken word, beyond doubt, being more understandable, has a profounder effect, as may be judged by the surprising emergence in casual talk of words that, until lately, were foreign to rustic speech, and by a general (and lamentable) flattening and pinching of the broad vowels which gave the local dialect its rich sonorousness, to the meaner dimensions current in that clipped cockney manner of speaking, which must, sooner or later, be accepted as Standard English.

Even when the Monk's Norton housewives are not consciously listening to these refined accents, they hear them and imitate; but, as often as not, when the human voice utters comprehensible words, they do listen, and listen intently. It is not music or drama or any other manifestation of the artistic impulse that appeals to these unlettered, bookless minds, but Talks—talks on every conceivable subject, from World Politics to Cage Birds and Jam Making. It is doubtful if, before the coming of "the wireless," the women of Monk's Norton were conscious except through the weekly newspaper or by laggard hearsay of the events of contemporary history in their own country, to say nothing of "foreign parts." Now, no sooner has any incident that makes "news" occurred in any corner of the five oceans or continents, than the loud-speaker forces them to hear of it and to take note of it. Living voices bawl at them in a familiar tongue from the United States, from South Africa, from the Antipodes. Even if the domestic affairs of Monk's Norton still seem more important and more interesting, they have become aware, in spite of themselves, of the existence of an outer world, and feel, however faintly, the impact of the shocks that disturb it. And this general awareness, unconscious though it may be, has had the effect of exciting their curiosity as to people and things and places about which, in the past, they have had no concern, flattering them, as they put their fragments of knowledge together, with a sense of not being so ignorant as they had supposed themselves, and awakening, by degrees, an appetite for mere information (not necessarily valuable) about most things under the sun. If the wireless talks have not actually enriched their minds, they have certainly widened them more rapidly than their husbands'.

So, with more digestible food, has the Women's Institute, to which Mrs. Sheldon-Smith and Miss Abberley graciously lend their patronage, and Miss Martin, Nurse Burlingham and the rector's wife, Mrs. Follows, their active collaboration. The Women's Institute meetings are held in the Village Hall, and are the principal justification for that abominable building's existence.

Their prime purpose in the case of Monk's Norton—though the ladies who started them would honestly and indignantly deny it—was a subtle and indirect form of political propaganda unnecessary before the working-man's wife got a vote: an attempt to prove that the colonel's lady and Judy O'Grady were sisters, that the gulf which unhappily separated their standards of living was quite unimportant compared with their fundamental community of sex, and that if only the women of both classes could "get together" and understand one another—without talking or even dreaming of politics—all these small, accidental, unavoidable differences could be smoothed away in an atmosphere of pure and friendly reasonableness, with the inevitable result that no wife would vote—or allow her husband to vote—for a labour candidate.

It was in these terms, no doubt, that Mrs. Sheldon-Smith and that crafty old lady, Miss Abberley, thought when they first gave their patronage to the Monk's Norton Women's Institute. Yet good results may come from intentions which, if not precisely evil, are not wholly disinterested; and that was what happened in this case. Miss Abberley was too old and too much of an invalid to take any active part, and Mrs. Sheldon-Smith's attempts at being a "good mixer," with all the good-will in the world, were not very successful; so that the task of putting the Women's Institute on its feet was left to the rector's wife, who had no politics to speak of, and to Miss Martin, who was a member of a trade union, and a moderate Socialist: the two people best qualified by nature and inclination to do the job.

And, once set on its feet, the Monk's Norton Women's Institute, which has no particular bias in any direction, is perfectly able to stand by itself, for the excellent reason that, for the first time in their lives, apart from casual visits and doorstep gossip, it has given the women of the village the chance to meet and talk and be jolly, to forget, for a while, the drudgery of a housewife's calling, and to realize that their own conditions of life are much like their neighbours'. It has done more than that. It has awakened new interests, more personal than any they can extract from "wireless" talks, which after all, are didactic and not always within their grasp—whereas Miss Martin, and Mrs. Follows and the ladies who come to speak to them from neighbouring institutes are open to questions and ready to give explanations. It has become, among other things, a school of domestic economy, in which women who (like the majority) have married without any qualification for housekeeping apart from what they have picked up for themselves in a haphazard upbringing, are taught that the capacity for running a house is not given to them in the natural order of things or theirs by the grace of God, but may be acquired by instruction. It has interested them, too, in the revival of a number of home-industries, by which, in their leisure moments, a woman and her children can add to the family income; and out of these interests there has arisen a sense of pride in the things they make, and an intense but friendly rivalry—not only within the membership of their own institute but also with the members of others whose handiwork and packed produce they can admire for themselves in the market and exhibition held in the Shire Hall at Worcester, where ingenuity and industry and months of planning reveal themselves in two dozen decorated stalls beneath the embroidered streamers of Wychbury and Bromsberrow and Stourton and Chaddesbourne d'Abitot (which includes Monk's Norton), Temeford and the rest: each village determined to show the others what it can do.

And beyond all—though this influence is so subtle that hardly anybody realizes it—the Women's Institute has become one of the bases from which Nurse Burlingham conducts her unflagging sanitary crusade: not so much by direct suggestion as by the fact of her friendly presence among mothers—or mothers-to-be—whose problems she would otherwise never know, or who would be too diffident to call her in or go out of their way to approach her. She is always there, though generally rather late, bustling in with her bright antiseptic face and her radiant cleanliness, ready to listen to a whispered question or confidence, or to snatch at the opportunity of giving advice or a hint when either is needed; so that the Institute, through her, performs some of the functions of a consultative clinic of the kind which Dr. Hemming has always prayed for but never hoped to achieve.

The old women who spend their declining days in the cottages "down the road" may sniff at the younger generation "gadding off" to the Village Hall and leaving their poor men to get their own teas on a Monday evening. In their days, they say, a woman's whole duty on Mondays was to see to her washing, and her place was "in the home"; but their own homes would have been brighter and healthier and more orderly, their men better cared-for and their lives more interesting to-day, if there had been such a thing as a Women's Institute in the "good old times." And, of course, despite all the pious political hopes of the Abberleys and Sheldon-Smiths, the married members continue to vote in the same way as their husbands.

The Monk's Norton men are less well provided for in the matter of recreation than their sisters and wives. They have a Men's Club, which meets in the Village Hall on Wednesday evenings, but which has never flourished or become an influence like the Women's Institute. The older men are less sociable than the women; after a certain age they prefer their own gardens or firesides to the company of their fellows with whom they have been working all day. The women regard the Institute as an escape from their homes; the men regard their homes as an escape from their work. What is more, while the Women's Institute is still attractive as the exciting symbol of a recent emancipation, the men have always been able to go where they like, and therefore, out of natural perversity, prefer to stay where they are, and find it rather a relief, for once in a way, to be left to themselves. They are also, in general, less serious-minded and more easy-going than their wives.

For these reasons, in spite of the life which the rector and Captain Grafton have done their best to infuse into it, the Club is not a very vital affair. Its members are always a trifle subdued if not intimidated, through no fault of his, by their consciousness of the rector's cloth, the sight of which purges their speech of the meaningless but avowedly indecent expletives that are a natural part of it, and makes them awkward; while to those of them who have known the captain as their scoutmaster ever since they were breeched, his limited repertory of patriotic and manly sentiments has begun to pall. They have most of them reached an age when they feel it their duty to absolve themselves from the accusation of being namby-pamby or soft, an age at which a game of darts in the bar of the "Sheldon Arms" appears more attractive, because it is more adventurous, than the same diversion in the bleak or artificially cheery atmosphere of the Village Hall. Furthermore, they have come to the age at which they have begun to think about girls, when the pursuit of this natural quarry is more exciting and gives them a prouder sense of maturity than the company of their own sex or the innocent diversions devised by the rector and the captain to keep their hands and minds out of mischief.

That is why the Men's Club has a stigma of mildness and moderation attached to it, and is only patronized as a last resort, while those activities associated with the Village Hall at which girls are present are eagerly attended. Such is the Choral Society, founded and conducted by Miss Martin, which meets once a week for practice on Tuesday evenings in winter, and gives its annual performance about the time when the cuckoos arrive. Though Miss Martin seriously imagines herself an apostle of culture, the real reason for the success of her Choral Society is not, as she hopes, that Monk's Norton is becoming musical, but because young women attend the practices as well as young men. The village, in fact, is not "musical" in her sense of the word, and probably never will be; but the singers, particularly the basses, make up in enthusiasm and vigour for what they lack in sensibility. When they sing, they open their mouths and lift up their voices for all they are worth and let go a sheer crashing volume of sound that bids fair to lift the galvanized roof off the Village Hall.

Miss Martin has long since abandoned any attempt to make them sing softly, so she tactfully chooses for their performance such hearty outbursts as the Hallelujah Chorus from the *Messiah*, and the frenzies of the Priests of Baal in Mendelssohn's *Elijah*, in which the basses, led by the captain, can let off their steam. Her greatest success up till now has been last year's performance of Stanford's *Sea Songs*, and a mild bacchanalian work by Hubert Bath called *The Wedding of Shon Maclean*, though the text of the second gave rise to a schism that cleft the whole village and nearly wrecked the Society. At one point in the progress of the wedding festivities, the basses were required to interject, *fortissimo*, the single word "Whisky," which the captain and his stalwart companions bawled out with such evident gusto that

Mr. Webber, who is the leading spirit of the Band of Hope and the Rechabites, threw up his score and resigned from the Society in dudgeon and righteous disgust. Neither in word nor in fact, he declared, would he permit the abominable thing to cross his lips and become, thereby, an agent of vice and corruption. The captain did not improve matters by the facetious suggestion that, to salve his conscience, Mr. Webber should be allowed to sing the word "Cocoa" instead. Immediately the village was split by a controversy more fierce than any that had stirred it since the days when Fred Perry proposed to destroy the oak on the green. The captain would have his little joke, but this matter, because it involved not merely a moral principle but the village's reputation for decency and sobriety, could not be treated so lightly. Nobody would have dreamed that in such a small space so great a mass of combustible material existed. The question was debated, flippantly at the "Sheldon Arms" and gravely at the Women's Institute, while Mr. Webber, who, until then, had been regarded as an eccentric but rather harmless old man, assumed, in a night, the quality of a hero, if not of a martyr. "The righteous are called on to testify to the Lord," Mr. Webber maintained, "and testify I did and I shall!" The whole village, indeed, took sides with such intense feeling that at the following Tuesday's practice the benches occupied by the tenors, the altos and the sopranos were half-empty. Only the basses, encouraged by Captain Grafton, showed (apart from Mr. Webber's defection) an unbroken front, and bawled out the offending word with such hearty unanimity that as soon as they opened their mouths no other part could be heard. The balance of her chorus, in fact, was so disturbed and the work so mutilated that Miss Martin, overwhelmed by the basses' thunder, put down her baton and confessed that it was useless to go on.

At this point it became clear to everybody that, unless the matter were settled, the Choral Society itself must come to an end; and this, no doubt, would have happened had not Miss Martin, in desperation, induced the rector, as the obvious arbiter of all moral questions, to come to its aid.

It was no use, Mr. Follows knew, attempting to persuade Mr. Webber: as a nonconformist he did not acknowledge the rector's authority, and as a village Hampden he could not in honour retreat; but Mr. Webber's followers, most of whom were only too anxious to go on singing if only their consciences would allow them, were more amenable to argument. After all, Mr. Follows told them, the theme of the work was a Highland wedding, and whisky, however regrettably, was the highlands' traditional beverage, strictly comparable to the wine that was drunk at the wedding at Cana in Galilee. What was more, though to sing the word "whisky" might not be in the best of taste, and might excusably offend the susceptibilities of sensitive people, it was not equivalent to imbibing it in large quantities or likely to persuade other people to take to drink; while strong spirits in medicinal doses were acknowledged by most of the medical profession as legitimate and valuable drugs. On the whole, considering the innocuous nature of the rest of the work, and the time and trouble which had already been devoted to practice, he did not think that Mr. Webber's supporters need hesitate to perform it. If they still felt strongly, he could only advise them—not, of course, to accept Captain Grafton's facetious suggestion of an alternative, but merely to hum the tune at the point where the objectionable word occurred. So the matter was settled, and *Shon Maclean's Wedding* had as great a success as the *Wedding of Hiawatha*, at which, since there is fortunately no allusion to strong liquor contained in it, Mr.

Webber assisted next season without doing violence to his conscience.

The Choral Society, though plenty of young people belong to it, includes in its roll of membership a large number of the middle-aged, who find another favourite diversion in the whist-drives that are also held from time to time in the Village Hall. If money is wanted in Monk's Norton for any charitable object, the easiest way of raising it is to offer its inhabitants of every age the opportunity of sitting down comfortably to play cards and the chance, if their luck is in, of getting their own back in the shape of much personal glory and some trifling prize. Everyone in the village plays old-fashioned whist, the game of "grave simplicity" Mrs. Battle played, in which the suit of the last card turned up in the deal is trumps. The Russian variety which corrupted the ancient tradition in the eighteen-nineties under the name of Bridge-whist has no more succeeded in taking root in Monk's Norton than its more recent complications, Auction and Contract, of which most of the card-players in the village have not even heard. Captain Grafton has tried his hardest to introduce Bridge, but the old hands will have none of it; they are as jealous of the forms of their favourite game as Mrs. Battle herself.

When a whist-drive is held in the Village Hall you may find at the tables old people who never appear at any other public function, addressing themselves to the game with an intensity and a determination of which you would not have dreamed them capable.

Yet popular as the whist-drives are, and though young people join in them out of love for any social excitement available, whist is not much of a young man's (and less of a young woman's) game. Their passion—like the passion of all the world since the war-generation was bitten by the tarantula—is dancing. No sooner has the notice of a dance been posted up on the board outside the Village Hall, than the boys and the girls of Monk's Norton start thinking of little else. The reason is obvious: any contact between young people of opposite sex in a community so small, where everyone's business is everyone else's, is exposed to observation and censorship; and the licence of a dance, in which they can clip one another boldly without fear of public interest or disapproval, is too good to be missed.

Not that Monk's Norton dances are licentious; on the contrary it would be hard to conceive any functions conducted with more ceremonious decorum or more regard for convention. So Captain Grafton discovered, to his surprise and discomfiture, when, attending his first Cricket Club Dance, and looking forward to "having a bit of fun with the girls," he found that not one of the partners whom he had expected to provide it would budge a single step beyond the door with him. As soon as the music stopped they left him empty-handed, and returned to the company of other girls on the benches from which his hungry eyes had selected them. They had come to the dance to dance, and that was the end of it. He found also, when he attempted to "liven things up," that the "kitchen-lancers," to which nobody objected at Hunt Balls, were, according to Monk's Norton standards, considered indecorous—as, by any decent standards, they undoubtedly are.

There were other things that astonished him, and would probably have astonished most other people of his age and class, unaccustomed as they were to the slovenly shuffle that passed for dancing in those days. In addition to performing the fox-trots and two-steps which were the captain's habitual prelude to what he called casual poodle-faking, and the waltzes and jolly polkas he had danced in his more innocent boyhood, these village folk could find their way unerringly through the formal figures of Quadrilles (which were quite beyond him) and tread a swinging Mazurka or a sprightly Schottische—to say nothing of such odd inventions as the Veleta, a novelty of the early twentieth-century which, extinct elsewhere, has taken root and continued to flourish in the Monk's Norton soil. When the music struck up for these, the captain was forced to look on with envious eyes, or, pretending unconcern, to slink off to the dingy cloakroom (that smelt like a farmyard because of the young men's overcoats) and take a solitary swig from his flask to keep up his spirits.

It was not merely that these rough lads and their partners knew the steps and figures of dances he did not know. Those clumsy-looking feet, accustomed to the clodded plough, could actually perform them with more skill and more grace and a livelier sense of rhythm than his in their patent leather. Though their faces remained preternaturally solemn—for this was a serious and highly technical matter—and nobody spoke, the captain was forced to confess that their movements made him look clumsy; and when he danced with neat-footed, slim-ankled Miss Martin he felt like a boor.

He would probably have got on a good deal better with the Miss Sheldon-Smiths; but the ladies of the village rarely patronize these popular functions by their presence, and, when they do so, never take the floor—as poor Captain Grafton discovered to his humiliation when once—only once—fortified by an extra nip of whisky, he asked the elder of the two sisters for the honour of a dance and was coldly turned down. The rector and Mrs. Follows appear at these dances now and then, on occasions when the proceeds are to be devoted to some parochial fund or charity, and have even been known, amid salvoes of hand-clapping, to dance the Blue Danube together on a floor that has been cleared for the rather painful spectacle in accordance with the protocol observed in the case of Royalty at a State Ball. Though he realizes the potential danger to his parishioners' morals, he is ready to admit that dancing is a healthy exercise, and to regard these functions as a sort of safety-valve, if cautiously opened. Young people, he confesses, will "get together" anyway; and it is safer that they should "get together" decently, in the public eye and under the hanging oil-lamps, than among the haycocks beneath a lascivious moon. Even so, there is no building in Monk's Norton with more romantic associations than the concrete Village Hall with its galvanized iron roof—with one possible exception: and that, of course, is the Church.

THE CHURCH

VIII

The Church

THE church of the Archangel Michael, with its pinnacled squat perpendicular sandstone tower, stands back from "the Cross" on the opposite side of the lane from Miss Abberley's. It is not, architecturally, a remarkable building, being more or less of the type of a dozen others that serve similar scattered villages of the red marls. Its most prominent feature, the western tower, a relatively recent replacement of an earlier bell-turret of timber, is built in three stages, with angle buttresses and an embattled parapet, of lateish fourteenth or early fifteenth century workmanship, and is a structure so modest in height that when the great elms are in leaf it can hardly be seen.

In the belfry itself hang two bells of the same date as the tower: a treble and a tenor, the former slightly cracked. Neither the name nor even the initials of the founder appear on them; but a resolute explorer (Mr. Jagger, for instance) who cares to grope his way up the cobwebbed spiral to that haunt of fat-bellied spiders and bats hanging head-downwards, may decipher in the faint light of the belfry louvres (obstructed on the south by the hanging of a Sanctus bell which has disappeared) two inscriptions moulded in Latin: the treble's adjuring St. Peter:

SOLVE JUBENTE DEO TERRARUM PETRE CATENAS,

and the tenor celebrating, in a rhymed Leonine hexameter, the praise of its patron, St. Michael:

AD LAUDEM CLARE
MICHAELIS DO RESONARE

Both, but for the fissure in the treble, which also strikes the hour, are of sweet-toned metal, with a heavy proportion of copper to tin. Their two voices, one measuring the hours of man's life and the other, with its deep "hum-note" proclaiming with solemn knell his mortality, are, above all other familiar sounds, the voice of the village. They speak of its littleness and its humility; the unequal duet has a pitiful quality, as of something lost and deserted and out of the world, and the melancholy of the note of a bell-buoy tolling in estuarine fogs.

Mr. Follows often regrets that the tower does not hold a nobler peal such as might challenge the sky and the indifferent earth with a more splendid summons and proclamation of the glory of God. There are hangings for three more bells, as well as the Sanctus; but whither or when they vanished, or who stole them, not even Mr. Jagger can tell. It is the greater pity because, in the parish, there is a team of hand-bell-ringers who emerge towards Christmas, with Mr. Ferris, the blacksmith, that performer on tinkling anvils, as their "conductor," and ring changes—Plain and Treble Bobs and Grandsire Triples and Stedmans and complicated Surprises—to the tune of ten thousand on their silvery, singing chime.

There is something, after all, Mr. Follows is comforted to feel, in his little church's simplicity. The aisleless nave and chancel, of which the whole church was originally composed, were built, as the abbey rolls show, in the late twelfth century. Of this building only part of both walls of the nave and the south door, with its round, chevroned arch, remain; yet such are Time's powers of assimilation that no uninstructed eye would suspect that two centuries separate the stonework of these relics from that of the tower and of the south chapel, which flanks the Norman door and contains Miss Abberley's boxed pew and her family tombs. All are built of the nearest workable material, the pinkish grey sandstone quarried in the north of the county, the huge blocks resembling those in the ashlar base of the Goodrest's triple chimney-stack which, themselves, quite possibly may have been stolen from the remains of the fourteenth-century church-builders' dump; and the floors of the nave and chancel are flagged with sandstone too, diversified, on the risers of the altar-steps, by heraldic tiles, bearing the arms of Clare, Beauchamp, Cantilupe, Sheldon and d'Abitot, whose glowing encaustic has been saved by their upright position from the hobnails of twenty generations of Monk's Norton villagers.

These tiles, with their grounds of madder-coloured clay, of rich browns and tawny yellows, and their incised patterns of white, are the only ornament in the original building's austere interior. Its walls are pierced by lancets so narrow and so sparing of light as to explain why they have been whitewashed; and even the east window itself is composed of three more lancets, grouped under a pointed head, so slender that the few fragments of old stained glass which remain in them sparkle out of the end of the tunnel of masonry like fragments in a kaleidoscope. Not one of the Norman tombs, if such there were, remains.

In the nave there are no mural tablets. Only in the south chapel, where stands Miss Abberley's boxed pew, with its plump red cushions and hassocks and even an iron stove in front of which she may toast her feet in winter, the last ditch (or pen) of feudal privilege, may there be seen an efflorescence of (so appropriately!) eighteenth-century monuments commemorating in Johnsonian epitaph the virtues of the ancestors with whom she has so much—including that pew—in common. The wall of the pew is so high that, when the old lady is seated, no lesser eyes than those of Mr. Follows in the pulpit may behold her devotions or know when she has loosened her boots or fallen asleep; and, until she dies, there is not the least probability of any profane attempt to obtain a faculty and sweep that undemocratic preserve away.

Mr. Follows is proud of his little church—very nearly as proud of it as is Mr. Jagger. He would like, if he could, to have a vestry more comfortable than the curtained base of the tower whose imperfect privacy he shares with the sexton and the choirboys: a small square cluttered with musty vestments and surplices and woolly bell-ropes, to say nothing of the massive stone font set right in the middle. He would like—for he happens, in a mild way, to be musical—to find a better organ than the mouse-infested instrument from which Miss Martin, pedalling with all her might, produces such a meagre volume of sound. Mr. Follows would like to throw back his head and close his eyes and hear the lions roaring after their prey and seeking their meat from God in the Psalms, as well as the *vox humana* echoing angelic voices of cherubim and seraphim; but Miss Martin's lions are tame beasts at the best, and her shrill angels lack tenderness, and there is not even money to spare for repairing the fabric of the church or the crumbling pinnacles on the tower, which are actually becoming dangerous, let alone for such a purely æsthetic luxury as a new organ.

There is no money for anything, he sometimes thinks with a sigh; though the living, according to local standards, and to such fierce critics of the established church as Mr. Webber, is handsomely endowed. Five hundred a year looks all very fine on paper; but when that sum has been docked by a fifth in income-tax, the result is four hundred; and maintaining a huge, icy barrack of a rectory with no less than twelve bedrooms (but no bathroom) and dry rot in the roof on four hundred a year is no easy matter. It is impossible, everyone admits, to run this enormous house properly—even though Mrs. Follows herself works harder than any servant—with less than two maids; and two maids, with country appetites, account for another hundred. It is equally impossible for the rector to shepherd his flock (as he does, conscientiously) and, single-handed, keep nearly three acres of garden in order, to say nothing of maintaining the house and the crumbling outbuildings in repair. The old man who helps him, and also acts as sexton, costs the rector thirty shillings a week, which, deducted, reduces his income to less than half of the handsome living which he is supposed to enjoy. In the end he is left with only a little more than the pay of a skilled mechanic, or than that of Police Constable Homes (who is "kept" in boots and uniform, and has a house given him which is an asset, not a burden, and can look forward to a pension as well) out of which he is expected (and desires) to "keep up appearances" in the modest manner befitting a clergyman and a gentleman, and to give his son—there is only one, thank heaven—the sort of education his father enjoyed before him.

His critics, who include not only Mr. Webber but a good third of the village, are merciless. That astronomical figure of five hundred pounds obsesses them. It is ridiculous, they say, for the rector to sigh over the burden of a fine house like that. If it is really too big for him—and you needn't tell *them* he's not proud of it!—why doesn't he shut up two-thirds of it and reduce his establishment and live according to his means? Five hundred a year? Why, "the Reverend Winter" at Chaddesbourne, gets only three-fifty, and he a Rural Dean; while there isn't a Baptist or Wesleyan minister within miles who wouldn't jump at the half of such a benefice!

Mr. Follows has often thought of shutting up most of the Rectory; but he realizes, as his critics do not, that an empty house deteriorates. The dry-rotting roof, for which he knows he is responsible, is enough to be going on with; he will not take on any more risks. Nor is he, it must be granted, unduly querulous, though one might fancy that it is the weight of this Rectory that gives his shoulders their slight stoop and furrows his high and rather narrow forehead under the biretta he wears to keep the draught off his natural tonsure when he turns his back on his troubles and crosses the road to the church.

Even when he thinks most hardly of the Rectory he cannot help remembering the thrill he experienced when first he set eyes on it, at Miss Abberley's invitation, sixteen years ago. If it were not for the virginia-creeper that smothers it and the overgrown laurels and conifers that hide its façade and which, if he could afford the time and the money to pay for felling and uprooting them, Mr. Follows would certainly destroy, the sight of the Rectory would add to the dignity of the Cross. It was built, to the taste of an ecclesiastical Abberley, of the same material as The Grange, but a little later, and is a pure example of the Queen Anne style: a square, solid three-storeyed building with rows of well-proportioned windows and bricked-up apertures where, but for the tax, other windows would have been. Since Mr. Follows came to live there it has never been adequately furnished, for he was too poor to buy the curtains that went for a song at his predecessor's sale, and the filling of such an enormous window-space with new ones was beyond his most extravagant dreams. As a makeshift, which has become permanent, Mrs. Follows ingeniously fitted the windows in the rooms they try to occupy with lengths of casement-cloth which, though they exclude little light, give these handsome chambers an odd air of nakedness, dismally heightened by the fact that the squares of carpet which had been more than enough to give comfort to the little house her husband occupied as a Black Country curate were too small to cover more than a quarter of the space that awaited them, and now lie pathetically marooned, as it were, in the midst of a wide expanse of echoing floor.

The same fate has befallen the Follows' furniture, which was neither sufficient in quantity nor suitable in style to give even a semblance of filling or fitting its present surroundings. One has the feeling, indeed, that the nobly-proportioned rooms despise it, and dissociate themselves from its presence and that of its owners with a bleak and mournful detachment that chills the spirit. The house feels always empty and always cold. For some unexplainable reason (for the Follows are not vegetarians, and the kitchen is certainly forty icy yards from the front-door) it smells strongly of cabbage-water and faintly of drains. One has a suspicion that the plumbing is not what it might be. But then, drains run deep and plumbers are predatory; so such subterranean matters are best left well alone.

There is at least one comfortable room in the house: the study in which Mr. Follows writes his sermons and spends most of his time. It catches the morning sun, and used to be known as the breakfast-room; and in its small compass the rector has been able to concentrate enough belongings (and these sufficiently personal) to establish himself as its owner and not, as he is made to feel in the rest of the house, an intruder allowed to remain on sufferance. There is a big writing-desk, with an inlaid top of ink-splashed American-leather, on which his father, who was also a parson, wrote sermons before him. There are several deal bookcases laden with books: an average theological and a fairly representative classical library. There are the two easy chairs, upholstered in a Morris print (its pattern is called Kennet), whose vegetable indigos refuse to fade, which he bought with a minute legacy from an aunt in his second year at Worcester College, Oxford. One may see, on a tin shield flanking the mantelpiece mirror, as well as on a brown earthenware tobacco-jar which stands on his desk, the bearings of that foundation, and on another tin shield, hung symmetrically, those of Bromsberrow school. There are no pictures on the walls, but a number of large framed photographs: one of Worcester Cathedral with the glove-works' chimney in the foreground; one of a dumpy, bearded clergyman, looking rather like Anthony Trollope, who was the rector's father, and two Rugby football team groups, in which (though one would hardly believe it), the stalwart young man in the striped jersey holding the ball is an earlier incarnation of the rector himself. Against the only wall that is free from books stands a cottage piano laden with a pile of ragged music which includes Schubert's Songs, Hymns: Ancient and Modern, the Sonatas of Beethoven, and, rather surprisingly, a piano-score of *Die Walküre* (which is concerned with a theme not unknown in country districts), and another of *The Mikado*. In the corner opposite the piano Mrs. Follows has a little writing-desk of her own, not merely for the sake of her husband's company but because, in winter, his study is the only warm room in the house. Hers, too, are the flowers which, at every season of the year, she contrives to place in a vase on his writing-table; but the predominant odour of the study is not that of Mrs. Follows' flowers nor even of the *pot-pourri* jar which she fills every year—rose-leaves and orris and balm and sweet geranium, but the pervasive fragrance of a certain brand of Virginian honey-dew that Mr. Follows smoked at Oxford and still has sent to him by post, half a pound a month, from the same shop in the High Street.

This is the rector's only extravagance, his solitary luxury. It clings not only to his room but also to his clothes and his person, and is as proper to him as is its scent to a flower. Once or twice, in Lent, he has gone to the length of cancelling his monthly order; but the lack of the drug so frayed his nerves and made him so restless that his wife, who had approved of the sacrifice on economic rather than religious grounds, took the law into her own hands and secretly posted an order for a double supply and rejoiced in the cure of his haggard irritability.

This was not an isolated example of Mrs. Follows' wisdom and humanity. There is a strain of impetuosity in her husband, and an almost frantic bigotry in matters of principle which nobody but this plain and rather awkward lady can moderate. He respects her as much for her courage and strength, which are more deep-rooted than his, as he loves her for her constant, sweet serenity, her secret humour, and her unique understanding of what he believes to be the complications of his own nature. As a matter of fact this is not very complicated, except in so far as it is the nature of a child. The truth of the matter is that this lanky, middle-aged man, with his rather narrow forehead, his kindly blue eyes, and his radical goodness and innocence, has never grown up. He is still, in spite of his learning, which is considerable, and the knowledge of human nature he has acquired in his calling, essentially the stalwart young man who nurses the ball in the football team groups on the rectory study walls. That is why, for all his earnestness and his success as a devoted parish-priest, which most of his parishioners would allow him, he looks always a little puzzled, and, beneath the robust self-confidence he shows in public, is not quite sure of himself, and in blacker moments, which only his wife can lighten, considers himself a failure.

It is hard to say how far he is justified in this. If a rigidly upright and virtuous life and unceasing labour, if a delicate sense of personal honour and loyalty to the principles of his creed, combined with more charity towards human failings than most men of his cloth dare show, are enough, he is not a failure. But the truth remains that, in spite of these qualities, and in spite of the fact that he is both respected and popular, he has never, as he would desire, "got hold of" Monk's Norton. There is always some intangible but appreciable barrier between his people and him. Is it, he sometimes wonders, because he is classed as a gentleman? Does the dignity attached to that great house, which he would so gladly get rid of, intimidate them? Is it that the language he speaks, in which seemingly simple things like words have associations for him that they have not for them, is different from theirs? Is it merely the existence of a profound and instinctive suspicion implanted in their ancestral memories by unremembered social wrongs, no less than the injustices of to-day—so easy to accept and explain yet so hard to defend—that separates them? Is it sufficient for him, as a minister of the gospel, to preach the word of God (to "testify," as Mr. Webber would call it), to uphold his church's sacraments, to display, in humility, the example of a sober, righteous and godly life, and to leave the inferences to others? Or is it his duty, as a priest, to concern himself, not in general but in detail, with examining and influencing public opinion—(was it the devil who whispered "Politics?")—on issues material as well as spiritual, such as War and Peace, Dictatorship, Unemployment, Re-armament—those themes which the Church discreetly (or is it weakly?) retiring behind its veil of doctrine and sacrament renounces to the debate of the wave-stirred ether? Are not these the proper topics of Christian brotherhood? Should not the currency of his daily commerce bear the image and superscription of Cæsar as well as those of God?

All these questions Mr. Follows asks himself, striving for justification, and finds, for all his aspirations of good-will, no certain answer. He is a timid and simple man: apart from his wife and his son, a lonely man too. He has no friend in Monk's Norton or in the diocese to whom he can open his doubtful heart. Though he trusts in God and wrestles with Him in prayer, there are moments in which he hungers for more definite human direction, the afflatus (if that be not impious?) of some new Revelation, some new breath that shall trouble the waters. The sense of this lack pursues him when, bicycling or on foot, he traverses his parish, visiting the infirm and the sick, and passing the time of day in casual encounters. It pursues him most vehemently of all when the cracked treble bell is ringing, and, clad in his cassock, a lanky, black, tubular figure, with his slightly stooping shoulders and his puzzled mystic's eyes, he steps across the road from his monstrous rectory and threads his way over the winding path that is flagged with forgotten memorials of mortality, between the great carnivorous yews, whose wet bark is the colour of blood, and the broken tombs whose lids bird-sown elder has shifted, and enters the base of the tower where the choir-boys are chattering. It pursues him as he follows, with bowed head and folded hands, the humble procession that shuffles so slowly up the aisle and mounts the steps where the coloured encaustic preserves the achievements of Clare, and Beauchamp, and Cantilupe, and Sheldon, and d'Abitot; as he kneels and rises again and lets his mild gaze survey, with some personal pride as well as approval, the Sunday's congregation; as he opens his lips and hears his own refined voice, with its Oxford vowels, intoning:

"*Dearly beloved brethren* . . ."

And he really means it. But when he ascends the pulpit, the sermon he preaches is the paraphrase of a biblical text for the schoolchildren or some definition of doctrine for their elders—not a confession of the doubts that are burning his heart. And perhaps this is just as well, besides being much easier; for old Miss Abberley is there in her pen, and possibly awake.

For so small a village, the congregation is a large one. It is one of the feathers in Mr. Follows' biretta that he has never, like some neighbouring parsons, frightened it away. In Monk's Norton there has never as yet been a chapel to compete with his service by providing a more homely, if less brightly-coloured, form of free entertainment on a day when none other is to be found. A few of his congregation go to the parish church to worship. Such is Mrs. Bentley, the postmistress and, such, perhaps, Mrs. Hawley; for Mrs. Bentley, kneeling in church or listening to Miss Martin's music, feels nearer to "Father," and Mrs. Hawley needs some mystical consolation for her husband's carnal infidelities, though the offender, who has always been a regular churchgoer, sits at her side. There is also Miss Coningsby, most pious and steadfast defender of the faith, who has, somehow or other, escaped notice in this perambulation: not entirely without excuse, for her minute spinsterly cottage, next door to the Rectory, is, appropriately, a mere appanage, attached to and overshadowed by that building; and she herself is equally inconspicuous—a frail, tiny creature, with scanty grey hair dragged back into an exiguous bun beneath a black hat, resembling, in her hunched figure and darting movements (which are limited to a furtive "run" from her dwelling to the church and back again) a mouse, or one of the heraldic rabbits which decorate her family coat-of-arms. The Coningsbys, in their time, Mr. Jagger will explain, were considerable people with extensive lands in the north of the country, entitled to bear: *Gules, three sitting conies argent in a border engrailed sable;* but Miss Julia Coningsby, though she still possesses a few pieces of silver with these grandeurs engraved on them, does not concern herself with temporal pomps. Why she came to Monk's Norton or how she contrives to live there, nobody knows. From august names casually mentioned and certain faded photographs of young ladies in court-dress displayed on the mantelpiece of her little parlour, it is supposed that, in her youth, she was probably engaged as a governess in some noble family; her precise speech, too, has a suggestion of prunes and prisms; but whatever her avocation may have been in her prime, she is now the perfect church mouse, innocuous and obscure, with no other desire or ambition than to creep to and fro between her cottage and the altar-steps, and no other spiritual sustenance than the crumbs that fall from her hero the rector's table.

Apart from the service of the church she has no activities; but in such matters as the cleaning of the communion-plate and the altar-vases and the provision for these of flowers which she piously cultivates all the year round in her garden and green-house, she is endlessly useful. She is useful to Mr. Follows in another way. Whether it snows, blows, rains or hails, Miss Coningsby has never yet missed a celebration of the Holy Communion; and when, mounting the pulpit, doubtful of himself and conscious of the impenetrable reservations of the faces beneath him, he sees, up-turned in its accustomed place, Miss Coningsby's rapt countenance, he takes heart from the knowledge that here, at least, amid the indifferent or critical, is one humble soul who takes no count of his personal imperfections and sees in him only the anointed minister and instrument of Christ.

No other member of the morning congregation is quite so whole-hearted or single-minded as little Miss Coningsby; yet it includes, to the rector's satisfaction, the village's most sub-stantial inhabitants. The Collinses are always there in full force, and so, naturally, is the people's warden, Mr. Cantlow. The Sheldon-Smiths are regular in their attendance; for they know that it is part of the "county's" duty to set an example, and that the established Church is one of the main props of the state of society they desire to maintain. The captain is there, for much the same reason, and because he enjoys singing hymns; and the gnarled ancients with their shrivelled old women from "down the road" hobble up in their Sunday broadcloth, when the weather is fair, because they have always reckoned to go to church and enjoy a good gossip outside when the service is over. Dr. Hemming rarely attends, except at the major festivals of Christmas and Easter: the rector, although he mistrusts these evidences of a nominal conformance, excuses his absence on the grounds of a wider humanity, and has never yet dared to examine the doctor on his beliefs, while the reputation of his household is sustained in any case by the regular presence of his wife.

The Perrys, too, are usually in evidence, subconsciously anxious to make amends for their calling's questionable morality; and besides all these, more or less filling the narrow nave, there sits, pew behind pew, a mixed congregation comprising most of the children and, perhaps, a third of the adult population of the village, which, indeed, in these days of faith's decadence, is by no means bad. Mr. Follows knows every face and every name. He, himself, has catechized and prepared for confirmation most of these strapping red-faced lads in their Sunday serge, and the buxom girls in their summer silks and muslins. He is aware, as he gazes down at them, that what has brought them here is not so much the desire to worship (nor even the enjoyment of his eloquence) as an established habit of "going to church" on Sundays, and wearing their best clothes and seeing what others are wearing, and showing themselves at their best to members of the opposite sex; and this knowledge does not offend him, for he has been young himself, and considers it far better that they should come to church for these reasons than not at all. He is also not so young as he was, and feels, therefore, wistfully benevolent towards all these young folk who are falling or have fallen in love, for he knows now that there is nothing in human experience so sweet as that early bemusement, and that life is shorter than they can guess, and these fleeting raptures more precious. There is something infinitely hopeful and infinitely pathetic to him in their very youth, and their confident carelessness of what the future may hold for them. His tender heart prays, as he sees them, that the village which has grown so dear to him and which, in spite of his aspirations, he is conscious of serving so inadequately, may not be decimated by another war; but when the spirit moves him to speak his mind on Armaments or Pacifism or International Relations, he realizes that these subjects are almost as contentious as Birth Control, so that the hot words die on his lips, and he rehearses instead the morals that may be drawn from the familiar story of Daniel in the Den of Lions.

The young people, on the whole, are more interested in the evening service, which is shorter and brighter and includes neither sermon nor Litany. It is sweet, in late cuckoo-time, to emerge from the church's atmosphere of faint repression into the golden air of evening, so fair and so free, and to linger a short while talking under the lengthening shadows of the elms. This is the hour and the season of lovers. In its quiet release there is no sense of the stresses and preoccupations of the workaday world. So, when Miss Martin has finished her voluntary and shut the organ, and the rector, in his long cassock, has slowly crossed the street, and their elders stand talking in hesitant little groups at the Cross or move slowly down the road or the lane in a straggling trail, the young folk who are "walking out" discreetly sort themselves into couples and link arms and unobtrusively steal away.

This custom of Sunday night courting is as old as the church itself. There is a ritual attached to it, and certain roads and field-paths are traditionally devoted to its observance. There is, for instance, the brambly bridle-path commonly known as Love

Lane, which pursues a meandering course beginning at the back of the churchyard and rejoining "the lane" between the allotments and the watersplash. There is another circuitous route, beset with convenient stiles and swing-gates, which leads to the opposite extremity of the lane by way of the "cut" on whose towpath the patient fishermen from North Bromwich sit hunched on their stools in the attitude of Rodin's Thinker, too deeply rapt in the contemplation of motionless floats to notice the swish of a skirt or the tread of hobnails or to hear the whispered words that lovers utter. There is a third, and perhaps the most frequented of all (though even here tradition insists on a decorous spacing) which leads to the mill and traverses the dam at the lower end of the mill-pond to follow the shadowy vagaries of the Brandon Brook through the field called Jericho, to cross the road by the Goodrest gate and be lost in Long Dragon—beyond which, where the brook bends westward, it enters into the quietude of Pritchett's Wood, a foxy cover so secret that even the shyest of lovers may feel their embraces secure, since no eyes observe them close-locked in each other's arms save those of the bounding squirrel or a brown owl silently swerving between the tree-trunks, and no sound startles their kisses save the shout of a jay or the stock-eagle's ribald laugh.

A ghost walks, they say, in Long Dragon Piece, and crosses the path that runs through Pritchett's Wood—a solitary ghost: yet if, as some hold, such apparitions be naught but shadows cast upon a retentive ether by human emotions so intense that they cannot fade, then, surely, Long Dragon and Pritchett's Wood should be populous with the ghosts of dead loves without number. As indeed they are; for if you happen to mention that path in Monk's Norton the lips of the young may smile, but the eyes of old men grow distant and momentarily cease to see you, beholding, instead, the dim curves of Long Dragon in the dusk and smelling may or meadowsweet and feeling once more on their lips, now dry and wrinkled, the warm pressure of other lips which, perhaps, are dust.

In July, before evening mists begin to rise from the brook, the air is so mild and the twilight so long, that Sunday evening lovers are slow to leave these haunts and turn homeward. Long after the sun has gone down the moonless sky remains luminous, and when it has darkened, the meadows seem no less light; for not only are hedgerows heaped with motionless billows of elder-blossom, and ditches beneath them clogged with pale umbels of cow-parsnip and plumes of meadowsweet and night-scented campion-flowers, all of which imprison the ghost of departed light, but the very earth over which the linked lovers pass is drenched in a silvery phosphorescence of cut hay lying in swathes, and the milk-mild air that fans their hot cheeks as they go is peopled by luminous wings of gauzy ghost-moths silently eddying in a dance of death and of love as ecstatic as theirs, and only a little more brief.

At this time of the almost timeless twilight there is hardly a sound but the swish of their steps through the grass; the nightingales on the edge of the wood have long since fallen to silence.

Only, far away in the wastes of the upper sky beyond the Goodrest, they may suddenly hear the harshened note of a late-homing cuckoo.

"Cuck-cuck-cuckoo!" he sings, with a falling, tuneless note. The lovers stop and listen. "Cuck-cuckoo," he cries discordantly.

"Hearken to that there bird," the boy says. "He be later home nor us two. And his voice is all broke. I reckon he's thinking it's time to be going to Pershore Fair."

"Pershore Fair? Don't be soft, then! What would a cuckoo want going to Pershore Fair?"

"Why, to buy him the horse he be going to ride away on. Don't you know that?"

"Well, I never did hear such rubbish! Come on, Jim, we're late as it is, and mother will be wondering . . ."

POSTLUDE

POSTLUDE

IT is true that the unfortunate cuckoo has lost his voice and changed his tune. He was the one who, in April, dropped down to the pyramid of wild pear in Long Dragon Piece, and his stay in Monk's Norton, though strenuous, has not been satisfactory. The earlier days, after his tired arrival, were the most exacting; for though, as he expected, he found an abundance of caterpillars whose hairs now coat his smooth gizzard, there was also a plethora of combatant rivals who had left the long African grass a week before him, and were already courting the most desirable females. In the pursuit of these bubbling beauties he lost much breath and several feathers, but finally, having scattered the other suitors, settled down to a well-fed, undisturbed courtship that culminated in the laying of one green egg in a hair-lined hedge-sparrow's nest well-hidden in the middle of a thorn-bush in Mrs. Collins's garden. After that, neither he nor his wife, gave their progeny another thought. The rearing of the intrusive monster was the hedge-sparrow's business, not theirs. So, with no more thought of love-making, he devoted himself, as elderly parents will, to the delights of the table, leaving his wife and cramming his greedy gizzard with multitudes of drinker-caterpillars, making the blue sky echo with roisterous song, and losing his voice with over-use and indulgence.

The second cuckoo, who alighted on the lime at the Grange, found Mrs. Sheldon-Smith's garden not to his liking. There was hardly a single hen in the neighbourhood; and he had not flown five thousand miles to lead a bachelor life. It was a week before he succeeded in picking up a desirable partner; but, once having established relations, the hen found a suitable nest for the first of her eggs in a chaffinch's mossy cup wedged into the fork of one of Mr. Jagger's apple-trees. The nest was so carefully shagged with lichen that Mr. Jagger, whose sight is not what it was, would never have discovered it had not the monstrous changeling thrust its gaping head over the side and squawked for food. After that, he observed its behaviour and habits from day to day, and made notes on them, in his fine, clerkly hand, in the manuscript monograph devoted to the Birds of Monk's Norton.

The third cuckoo, who landed in The Cubbs, found the food supply inadequate; for the field had been heavily grazed by Harry Hawley's horses as well as by the bullocks and sheep he bought at Worcester market and kept here to pick up what living they could till they were ready for slaughter—with the result that the hairy caterpillars, awakening from their winter sleep, found no juicy provender and returned to their hibernation in the matted grass-roots, where they lay, in dew-spangled curls, awaiting the day when things would take a turn for the better. So that cuckoo, after much fruitless or poorly-rewarded labour, flew away to the Mill, where the grass already grew lush and the fields were not overstocked with Mr. Hallow's thin cattle; and the first of the eggs that he fertilized was laid in the feather-lined hole of a pair of pied wagtails who flirted their pretty tails and bobbed and ran daintily over the sands of the Brandon Brook in whose bank they nested. This cuckoo was the best-fed and most vociferous of the three. He sang so loudly that his note got on poor Mrs. Hallow's nerves; for it was the voice of love, which she yearned for, and the voice of the country, which she hated.

So they sang as they flew, these three cuckoos and many others, until hay-harvest came. Mr. Hallow harnessed his horses, and the Collins boys hitched the mowing-machines on to their tractors, and the clattering knives, revolving, filled the air with a corncrake sound. And as the machines passed to and fro between the fields' headlands, the proud heads of grass to which the hairy drinkers had clung (they were less plump and more horny-skinned now than they had been) were shorn and fell to the ground with a sighing sound; so that, within a fortnight—for, luckily, the weather held fair—there was not a field in the parish left unstrewn by fallen swathes, nor a single caterpillar in sight save in corners into which the machines could not sweep their knives—and even in these men were busy swinging their scythes. What was more, by this time the young birds were hatched and eager to forage for themselves, and the cuckoo population of Monk's Norton was threefold increased. In Long Dragon, which is never mown, a few wasted caterpillars remained; but what was this miserable supply among so many? The old cuckoos grew hungry and sullen, for they were used to fat living. As they harried the sky and cried with their harsh, changed voices, the land, which when first they alighted had stretched beneath them like one vast green sea, looked barren and bleached. Even the trees had lost their greenness. The heavy foliage of the churchyard elms was nearly as dark as that of the yews beneath them.

It was not much fun, the old cuckoos thought, to work hard for their living at their time of life and to dispute the little that was left with hordes of unmannerly youngsters, the progeny they had definitely disowned from the moment the eggs that held them were impregnated. So, one night, when the wind that blew from the north brought a nip of Arctic ice into the upper air, they made up their minds to leave the young fools to starve, and launched themselves on the drift of the southward current. "*Cuck-cuck-cuckoo . . . cack-cack-cack!*" they gabbled spitefully, with broken notes that were harsh as a magpie's cackle and expressed their scorn of the famished northern fields. "*Cack-cack-cack-cack . . . Cack-cack*," they shrieked.

And, next morning, they were gone.

Craycombe House,
1:10:36—7:11:36.